The Illustrated Book of
Guns *and* Rifles

The Illustrated Book of
Guns
and
Rifles

edited by Frederick Wilkinson

Optimum Books

Acknowledgments

People

Frederick Wilkinson and the publishers gratefully acknowledge the assistance of Magnum Arms Company, Wolverhampton, in the preparation of this book.

Photographs

Richard Akehurst, Oxted 109, 164–165 top; D.W. Bailey, London 52, 53, 66, 69 third from top, 69 bottom; Bavarian National Museum, Munich 30–31; Ian Bennett, London 26 bottom; British Museum, London 11, 74; Central Office of Information, London 137 top, 152 centre; Crown Copyright – reproduced with permission of the Controller of Her Majesty's Stationery Office 65 top, 112–113, 123, 127, 128; Photographie Giraudon, Paris 9; Gunshots, London 7 bottom, 13, 14 bottom, 15 bottom, 17 top, 21, 22 top, 24, 26 top, 32 right, 34–35 bottom, 36–37 top, 40, 41 bottom, 42, 43, 44–45, 45 bottom, 47 left, 47 right, 48 left, 48 right, 49, 50 top, 50 bottom, 51 bottom, 54 bottom, 56–57, 57 top left, 57 top right, 57 bottom, 58 bottom, 60 left, 60–61, 62–63, 64–65, 67, 68, 69 second from top, 72 top, 72 bottom, 76–77 top, 77 top, 77 bottom left, 77 bottom right, 78–79 bottom, 79 bottom, 82 top, 86 top, 87 top, 87 bottom, 89 bottom, 90 top left, 90 bottom left, 90–91, 92 bottom, 94–95, 95 right, 98 top, 98 bottom, 99, 100 bottom, 100–101 top, 100–101 bottom, 104–105 top, 106 top, 106 bottom, 106–107, 110 top, 110 bottom, 111 top, 111 bottom, 114, 115 top, 115 bottom, 116–117 top, 118, 122, 124, 125, 131, 132–133, 133 top, 133 bottom, 138–139, 139 top, 140, 142, 143, 146–147, 150–151, 152–153 bottom, 154 top, 157, 158, 159, 160, 162, 164 top, 166, 167, 168, 169, 172 top left, 173, 174–175 top, 174–175 bottom, 176, 182–183 bottom, 184–185 centre, 185 top, 187 top, 187 bottom, 188; Hamlyn Group Picture Library 7 top, 12, 15 top, 18, 19, 20 top, 20 bottom, 23, 33, 38–39, 46, 51 top, 54 top, 64 left, 66–67, 70, 71, 83, 84, 86 bottom, 91 bottom, 100 top, 102–103, 119 top, 126, 148 top, 154 bottom, 155, 156 top, 156 bottom, 170–171, 182–183 top, 184–185 bottom; Imperial War Museum, London 116–117 bottom, 118–119, 120, 129 top, 129 bottom, 134–135, 136, 137 bottom, 141, 144–145, 149; Victoria and Albert Museum, top; Koninklijk Nederlands Leger-en Wapenmuseum, 'Generaal Hoefer', Leiden 36 bottom; A.G. Lang & Co, London 73; Library of Congress, Washington 179 right; MacClancy Press, London 147 bottom; Metropolitan Museum of Art, New York 37 bottom; Musée de l'Armée, Paris 80 bottom; National Army Museum, London 10, 14 top, 184 top; W. Keith Neal, Guernsey 22 bottom, 25, 27, 32 left, 38 top, 41 top, 54–55, 58–59, 61 bottom, 78–79 top, 186; D.S. Penn, London 96 top; Radio Times Hulton Picture Library, London 96–97; Ann Ronan Picture Library, Loughton 69 top, 82 bottom, 177 top, 177 bottom, 179 left, 184 bottom; Syndication International, London 178; U.S. Embassy, London 76 bottom; U.S. Signals Corps, National Archive 88 bottom; Victoria and Albert Museum, London 81 top, 172 top right, 172 bottom; Wallace Collection, London 180–181, 181 top, 181 bottom; Weidenfeld and Nicolson, London 88 centre; Winchester Gun Museum, New Haven, Connecticut 88 top, 105.

Note: All the metric conversions used in this volume are the direct equivalents of the imperial units and, in the case of calibres, many vary slightly from conventional usage.

This edition published by Optimum Books in 1979

Filmset in England by Servis Filmsetting Limited, Manchester
Printed in Italy

Contents

Introduction

Frederick Wilkinson

Today most infantrymen are armed with a lightweight rifle capable of firing a small bullet with tremendous power over long ranges with great accuracy. Since the rifle is self-loading he can maintain a constant rate of fire by inserting full magazines. At night his rifle can be fitted with sights which enable him to pick out a target with the same ease as he would in the light of day. Some can be fitted with laser beams and the shooter simply moves the red dot of light until it is on target, presses the trigger and is virtually certain of a hit. The infantryman has at his disposal a range of specially designed bullets and many of the weapons can also be easily modified to act as a missile discharger. This efficient, powerful weapon is the end product of a line of development which stretches back to the fourteenth century.

The story begins in China in the eleventh century but in Europe firearms date only from the fourteenth century. It was during the sixteenth century that the foot soldier was equipped with a heavy, rather cumbersome firearm known as a musket. It was inaccurate, crude, heavy and often unreliable, but when hundreds of them combined to fire a volley of shots the effect was devastating. Slowly firearms began to dominate the battlefield until by the eighteenth century nearly all the infantrymen of Europe and America were equipped with these long muskets.

As engineering knowledge and skill improved so the gunmakers were able to improve the design of the muskets. More efficient firing systems were developed, the weapon was shortened and accuracy was improved. Rifled barrels gave far greater accuracy but their production was slow and costly and until the introduction of machinery to do the job they were a comparative rarity. However, from the mid-nineteenth century the increased production enabled most countries to arm their troops with rifles. By the end of the century the infantry of the world were mostly equipped with a magazine rifle of one kind or another, capable of up to 10 shots before it required reloading.

The impact of gunpowder and firearms in earlier times was not limited to the military alone for, as their potential was realized, hunters discarded the bow and arrow and turned to firearms both for hunting and sport. Shooting grew more and more popular during the sixteenth and seventeenth centuries, and keen marksmen spent large sums of money on elaborately decorated rifles. During the seventeenth and eighteenth centuries shotguns gained popularity, and many landowners paid large amounts for custom-made shotguns with top-quality barrels, fashioned in a variety of styles. Even today this is still true, and second-hand guns by such famous firms as Holland and

Holland, or Purdey, fetch prices running into thousands of pounds. To acquire a new gun means going on a waiting list several years long.

When new lands were opened up the early settlers depended on hunting for their supply of fresh meat; on many occasions they also had to defend themselves against hostile natives. Both situations made it essential to have firearms, and a flourishing market was created. Gunmakers in towns such as Birmingham in England and Liège in Belgium began to cater for this demand for cheap but reliable rifles and shotguns. Soon nearly every farmer and settler possessed a simple, serviceable firearm which might lack the decorative quality and refinements of the rich man's but was still quite adequate.

Inventors have been trying to improve the performance of firearms since they first appeared and some of the ideas have been, to say the least, unusual. Some, like the percussion system introduced by a Scottish clergyman, Alexander Forsyth, were to change the entire system of firing the weapons; others, like the steam and electric gun, were no more than ingenious ideas. All these and many other strange facts played their part in the long path which led from the cumbersome musket through to the sophisticated modern firearm. It is a story full of interest and colour and one which, it is hoped, the reader will enjoy.

Above

This painting by William Jones, *circa* 1830, shows an English gentleman of the period shooting woodcock with a double-barrelled flintlock. The method of holding the weapon differs from the fashion today, the left hand now being placed well forward along the stock.

Right

Guns of many nations and craftsmen.
From top to bottom.
Modern double-barrelled, over-and-under shotgun by Gebrüder Merkel.
Flintlock rifle by Fisher of London. The barrel has multi-groove rifling, and the weapon dates from the early nineteenth century.
Unusual Indian sporting gun with carved rosewood stock and silver brass decoration.
Spanish blunderbuss with oval barrel and silver inlay. It was made in the late eighteenth century.
Long, metal-stocked, nineteenth-century Albanian flintlock with miquelet lock, decorated with brass, ebony and mother of pearl.

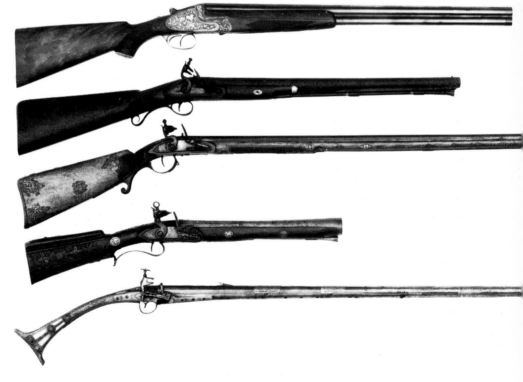

History and Development

Frederick Wilkinson

Among the differences which distinguish men from animals is the ability to attack from a distance. Animal combat involves close, physical contact and at first men fought in the same way but it was not long before they realized that being able to strike from a distance gave a considerable advantage. The sling, the bow and arrow, the great catapults of the classical world, were all developed to enable troops to hit at an enemy from a distance. However, the use of slings and bows and arrows required skills and co-ordination which not all men had. When confronted by fortifications, the only means of attack was physical force applied in the form of battering rams or by clambering over, through or under the walls. Anything which could enable troops to inflict damage on an enemy before they got close and could also demolish fortifications was obviously going to be very popular with the military. Gunpowder was to provide the means of doing both.

Gunpowder, or black powder, is a mixture of three components: charcoal (burnt or charred wood); potassium nitrate, or saltpetre, and sulphur. The best proportions of these components established by practice are about 75% saltpetre, 15% charcoal and 10% sulphur. When this mixture burns rapidly it generates a tremendous volume of gas and very large quantities of white smoke. Both saltpetre and sulphur occur naturally over much of the earth's surface and charcoal is, of course, readily available almost anywhere. Under what circumstances these three diverse components were first mixed is unknown but there is reasonably good evidence which points to that area of the world where it happened. Despite many odd, fanciful and intriguing theories there can be little doubt that modern research, particularly that by Professor Partington, has shown that China was the home of gunpowder.

There is fairly reliable evidence to suggest that the explosive compound was in use as early as the eleventh century. The Chinese, however, apparently did not at first realize the powerful force they had at their disposal and the earliest references suggest that the gunpowder was used more in the form of a diversionary weapon than as a means of discharging missiles. Perhaps laid in trails or confined in small clay pots, the surprise effect of the enormous flash and great cloud of whitish grey smoke when it was ignited must certainly have surprised and frightened attackers. Slowly the concept of using it to propel a missile was developed, and by about 1130 the Chinese were using a very simple form of barrel fashioned from bamboo strengthened by binding and known as a *huo ch'iang*. By the mid-thirteenth century the *huo ch'iang* was being used to discharge small pellets of clay or stones, and what may be described as the first firearm had been developed.

The route by which the knowledge of powder and guns reached the West is not at all clear. The most feasible explanation is that visitors from India and the Arab world, who maintained strong trading contact with the Far East, acquired the secret of gunpowder and it was carried by them along the trade routes until, eventually, it reached Europe. Just as the early history of gunpowder in the East is obscure, so equally obscure is the history of firearms in the West. There has been much discussion and learned research and it now seems reasonably certain that the first firearms in Europe do not predate the early fourteenth century. One of the more puzzling features in this quest for the origins of gunpowder in Europe is connected with the writings of Roger Bacon, a scholastic of the thirteenth century. He was a man of considerable scientific curiosity and he wrote a learned treatise on the secrets of nature, *De Secretis Operibus Artis et Naturae*. Contained in this book is one curious paragraph which has been construed to be a concealed anagram of the formula for gunpowder. However

French manuscript from the beginning of the sixteenth century showing cannon and musketeers in the front rank of troops. At this period gunpowder and guns were beginning to gain domination on the battlefield. Musée des Beaux-Arts, Nantes.

en mille chose de ce monde
ne se pourroit trouuer / mais
chascun de nous le cognoist
tard / et apres ce que en a
uons eu besoing. Toutes
fois vault encores mieulx
tard que iamais ✖✖✖

Sensuyt le commencent
des guerres qui furent entre
le duc de bourgongne et les
liegeois.

nsi se passeret
aucunes anees
durant lesqlles
le duc de bour
gongne auoit guerre chas
cun an auecques les liege
oys. Quant le roy le
voit empesche il essauoit
a faire quelque nouueaul
te contre les bretons / en
faisant quelque peu de
confort aux liegeoys.

the whole paragraph is open to question for in the earliest copy of the works of Bacon, dating from the thirteenth century, this paragraph is not included. It first appears in a printed copy of Bacon's work dated 1618. However, other references in Bacon's writings indicate fairly clearly that he knew of the effects of gunpowder, so the knowledge of gunpowder had presumably reached Europe by the thirteenth century.

As with the Chinese, gunpowder was not immediately used in the West as a propellant, but development took place and the first positive proof of the existence of firearms dates from 1326. The records of the Republic of Florence state that in 1326 two men were to be employed manufacturing ammunition and cannons. Of the same date are two manuscripts known as the Milemete manuscripts which were written by Walter de Milemete for the young King

Edward III. Although there is no mention in the text there appear, in the margins, two illustrations showing armoured knights apparently discharging vase-shaped cannons. There seems to be little doubt that these illustrations are contemporary with the manuscript and are not later additions. The mailed knight stands behind a wooden bench or table on which lies, apparently unattached, a vase-shaped object from the neck of which protrudes a point of an arrow. The knight holds in his hand a long, hooked rod which he is presumably using to ignite the gunpowder. The use of arrows in cannon was to continue, and stores listed in the Tower of London in the seventeenth century include such missiles. The shape of the vase is confirmed by a small, cast bronze cannon about 12 in (30 cm) long and of not dissimilar form, found at Loshult, Sweden in 1861.

Above
Close-quarter fighting during the Boer or South African War (1899–1902), when the British suffered many defeats from the accurate, long-range fire of the Boer rifleman. This print clearly shows the British troops armed with long Lee-Metford rifles. The majority of the Boers used German Mauser rifles.

Right
This small cannon is the ancestor of the hand gun. It is taken from a manuscript by Leonardo da Vinci.

To explode the gunpowder it has to be ignited, and quite how this was achieved in these early weapons is not clear. Possibly a metal rod could have been heated and the hot tip touched through a hole in the wall of the vase – the touch-hole. The problems involved with such a means of ignition would have been considerable. Some source of heating was necessary and, of course, the rod would quickly cool. Another and more likely system involved the use of some glowing material such as dried moss which could have been held or wound round the tip of a rod and then placed in the touch-hole.

Early references would suggest that the majority of these firearms were cannon or mortars used primarily to demolish defences such as castle walls. However, the concept of a metal receptacle loaded with powder and a shot in the form of a ball of stone, lead or iron was soon extended,

and the first hand guns were produced. They were little more than scaled-down versions of the cannon. Sometimes they had a long, thin extension from the breech end, (the solid, closed end), or they were cast with a socket at the breech into which could be inserted a wooden pole or stock. The weapons were loaded with a charge of powder followed by a ball and the end of the stock was then held under the arm, pressed against a wall or pushed into the earth and some means of ignition applied to the touch-hole to fire the shot. These weapons were crude and inaccurate but they had one advantage, they needed virtually no skill in their handling. Provided the guns could be supplied in quantity, groups of untrained men could be rapidly transformed into a formidable fighting force.

The big disadvantage of such hand guns, which was to remain with the

gunmakers for many centuries, was the fact that they were single-shot weapons. Once the weapon had been discharged, it was virtually useless until the gunner reloaded. There were various methods of solving this problem: one was to fit several hand guns together on a common stock. The guns were charged and one was fired; the group was rotated and the second fired, and so on. This system was to be used right through the early history of firearms.

With experience the gunmakers learned that the length of the barrel affected the efficiency of the weapon. Early gunpowder was very uncertain in performance as the proportions and quality of the sulphur, saltpetre and charcoal could vary. When subjected to constant, irregular movement such as the bouncing of a cart, the components tended to separate, so affecting the quality. Matters were improved by the introduction of corned gunpowder. The components were wet when mixed and then left to dry. They formed a solid block of propellant which was then crushed into grains. Even assuming that the quality of the gunpowder was kept constant, the fit of the ball within the barrel and the length of the barrel could affect the shot. If the bullet fitted tightly, the gases generated by the explosion were concentrated behind it and it was thus ejected with maximum force. If the bullet was a loose fit, then much of the gas escaped around the edges and so reduced its velocity. Gunpowder burns very rapidly but if the barrel is too short maximum pressure may not build up before the bullet leaves the muzzle. This means there is a loss of velocity and, up to a certain point, the longer the barrel the faster the bullet travels.

Ignition was another problem for the early gunners but it was not long before a partial solution was devised by taking a length of twine or cord and soaking it in a strong solution of saltpetre and allowing it to dry. If the cord was now lit it smouldered slowly with a glowing tip and a length of this cord, the match, could be kept ready to ignite the powder. By the very early fifteenth century a mechanical means of applying this match

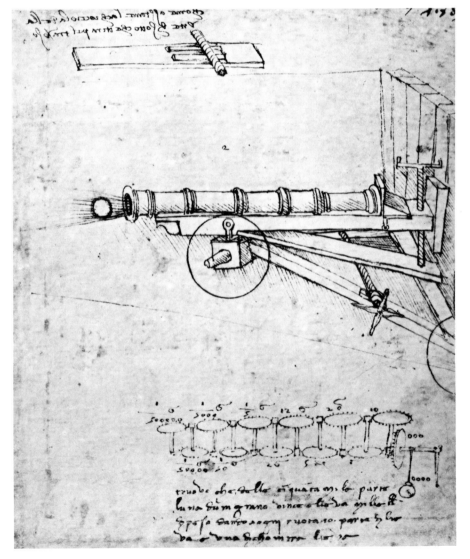

This print from a series known as the 'Triumph of Maximilian I', originally engraved in 1526, shows a group of Landsknechts with their short-barrelled matchlocks.

The searspring (1) presses down on the sear (2), ensuring that the serpentine (3) is held away from the pan. Pressure on the bar or trigger (4) activates the sear (2), which turns on the pivot (5), making the lug press down in the slot and forcing the serpentine to rotate. This forward movement brings the glowing tip of the match (6) into the pan. When the trigger is released, the sear is returned to the first position by the pressure of the searspring (1).

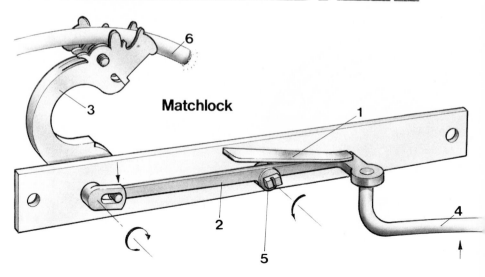

Matchlock

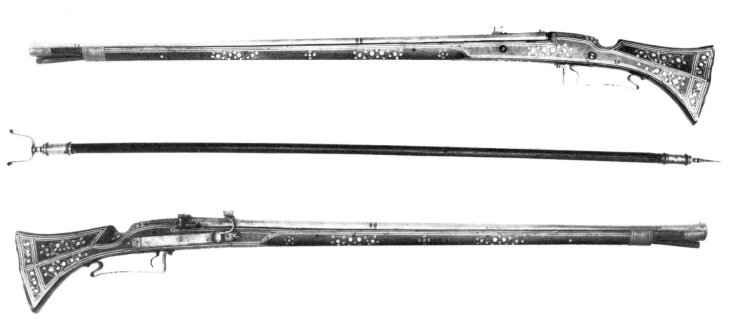

to the touch-hole had been devised, and because of its shape was known as the serpentine. It was a Z-shaped lever fitted to the side of the wooden support for the barrel, the stock. When the lower section of the serpentine was pressed upwards the upper section swung down and, as the match was secured to the end of the top arm, the glowing end was pressed into the touch-hole. Ignition was further facilitated by removing the touch-hole from the top of the barrel to the side and fitting a small projecting platform level with the touch-hole. Into this pan was placed a pinch of fine-grained powder, the priming, which was then ignited by the match and the flame passed through the touch-hole to set off the main charge.

The serpentine had now been developed into a simple but efficient mechanism called a matchlock. There were two forms: one was the snaplock, which was a somewhat dangerous mechanism having the serpentine so arranged that it was under the pressure of a small spring which held the tip of it down into the pan. When the musket was being loaded the serpentine was raised until it engaged with a small arm which held it in this raised position. When a trigger, or bar, situated below the butt was pressed, the sear was released and the pressure of the spring pushed the nose of the serpentine and the match down into the pan. The other form, which was to prove the safer, was the tricker or

trigger lock. This differed from the snap in that the pressure of the spring held the serpentine permanently in the raised position, clear of the pan. Pressure on the trigger or bar worked against the spring and depressed the head of the serpentine which again swung down to press the match into the pan. The pan was frequently fitted with a small pivoted cover, and if a pinch of powder was placed in the pan the cover could be closed to protect it from wind and weather. The stocks of these weapons were often inlaid with horn and mother-of-pearl.

Although these simple matchlock weapons varied in detail all conformed to a basic pattern but were known by a variety of names. Hackbut or arquebus was common

Both sides of a sixteenth-century matchlock musket and its rest. The matchlock is fixed on the right of the inlaid stock, and a ramrod is carried beneath the barrel.

From top to bottom
Unusual bronze musket barrel dated 1516 and carrying the arms of Von Schlabern Dorf.
Early seventeenth-century German wheellock.
Saxon wheellock rifle from the first half of the seventeenth century.

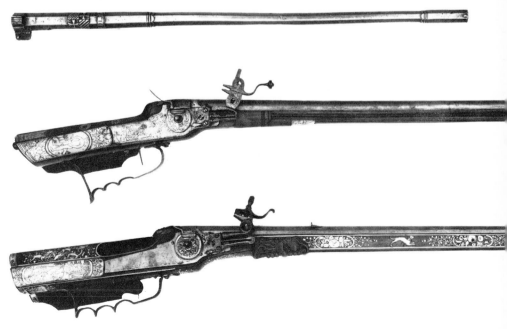

At the Battle of Pinkie in 1547, the musketeers operated around vast squares of pikemen, into which they retired to reload their weapons. This battle ended in a tragic defeat for the Scots.

but by the sixteenth century they were usually referred to as muskets. The name is probably taken from the Italian *moschetto*, a hawk, for it was common practice to name guns after birds. One big snag with the musket was its size, for the barrel was about 48 in (1.2 m) long and fired a ball some $\frac{3}{4}$ in (19 mm) in diameter. This long barrel made the weapon heavy and difficult for the musketeer to hold steady when aiming. The solution was to support the front end of the musket on a rest, a wooden stick which had a metal ferrule and a U-shaped metal attachment at the top.

By the end of the sixteenth century the musketeer was part of most European armies. He suffered from the great disadvantage that for a certain period of time he was so occupied as to be unable to defend himself. Once the musket was discharged the musketeer now stood with a useless lump of metal and wood in his hands until he had poured down a fresh charge of powder, inserted a ball, re-primed and brought the weapon back up into the firing position. He was totally vulnerable, and to protect him against the enemy cavalry groups of men with long pikes were interspersed with the musketeers so that, should the need arise, the pikes could be lowered to hold off cavalry.

The musketeer soon became encumbered with equipment. He had to carry powder, and at first only two methods were available although

Flemish or German musketeer's powder flask of 1581, made of wood with gilt copper metalwork. The nozzle has a mechanical cut-off which was operated to measure out one correct charge of powder.

later a third was added. Some carried a large wooden flask fitted with a metal nozzle equipped with a simple cut-off device permitting a charge of powder to be poured from the flask into the barrel. A second powder-horn or flask was necessary for the priming which was of finer-grained powder. Another method used small containers which held a previously measured charge of powder. These were of horn or wood and were suspended from a bandoleer or leather belt which went across the musketeer's chest. Normally the bandoleer supported 12 containers, and with his usual ironic wit the soldier christened them the 'twelve apostles'.

Quite early on a cartridge was developed which consisted of a tube of stout paper, hence the modern term 'cartridge paper', into which was poured the measured charge of powder together with the bullet which was either tied to or pushed inside the tube. To load, the musketeer bit or tore open one end of the cartridge, tipped a small amount of powder into the pan and then poured the rest down the barrel, followed by the bullet and the paper. He then pushed the whole lot home using a long wooden rod housed in a slot in the stock. The cartridges were carried in a leather box hanging from a belt worn across the shoulder of the musketeer.

When the musketeer was in combat he had to be prepared for instant action and this meant that the match must be kept burning constantly. It was common practice for the musketeer to carry flint and steel to re-kindle the match should the need arise, and he usually lit both ends of the match. One end was held in the jaws of the serpentine and the other was either wrapped around the stock or held in the musketeer's hand so that should one end be extinguished, another glowing tip was immediately available. This arrangement might be useful but it meant that the match was being consumed twice as fast as was essential, and consequently the musketeer had to carry a reserve supply. Sometimes he carried this inside his hat, or wound round its brim, or perhaps looped over his belt.

Above
Detail of the butt of a wheellock bearing the inlaid arms of the Marquard Von Hatstein Weilbach and dated 1605. The small metal ball was to protect the butt should the weapon be stood down. Victoria and Albert Museum, London.

Right
This engraving is based on one made by Jacob de Gheyn in 1609. The soldier is armed with a light version of the musket known as a caliver. He carries powder flasks, spare match, and a bullet bag hanging at his belt.

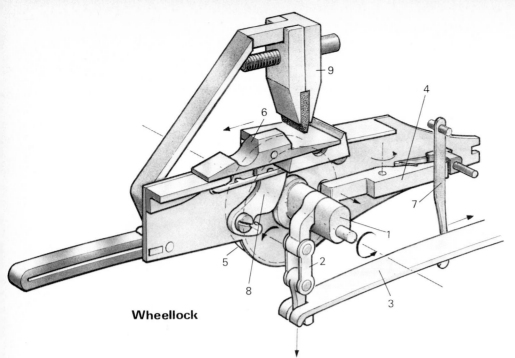

Wheellock

Left
A key or spanner is placed over the square-ended spindle (1) and rotated. This forces the transmission chain (2) to lift the arm of the mainspring (3). Spring-pressure causes the tip of the sear (4) to lock into a hole cut in the wheel (5). The pan cover (6) is pushed manually to the rear to cover the priming. When the trigger (7) is pressed, it releases the tip of the sear (4), and the wheel (5), under the impetus of the spring, turns in the direction indicated. As the spindle turns, it knocks a cam, the pan-cover arm (8), and this pushes the cover (6) forward, clear of the priming. The pyrites, held in the cock (9), presses against the wheel's edge and produces the sparks.

The match was, however, one of the basic weaknesses of this system: a sudden shower of rain, and virtually every musketeer in an army could be put out of action until a fresh, dry match had been supplied and re-kindled. On other occasions a sudden gust of wind might blow out the glowing end or, a far greater danger, blow sparks that might land on a companion's priming pan or, worse still, in an open keg of gunpowder.

The ignition system which, to a degree, supplanted the matchlock but never completely ousted it, was the wheellock. This mechanical device produced a shower of small, incandescent specks of steel. A piece of mineral known as pyrites and readily-obtainable almost anywhere in Europe, was held against the rotating, roughened edge of a steel disc to produce sparks. The wheel was rotated by a powerful, V-shaped spring which was usually coupled to the wheel by means of a short linked chain. The edge of the wheel was so positioned that it just projected through the base of the priming pan.

The mechanical operation was simple but involved a fairly complex mechanism. The wheel was mounted on a flat, steel plate set into the side of the stock. From the centre of the wheel projected a square axle and over this was placed a small, metal key, known as the spanner, which was turned and this rotation compressed the mainspring. At a certain point a spring-activated arm, the sear, pressed forward and engaged

with a small hole cut into the inside face of the wheel; the lock was now said to be spanned. Powder was placed into the priming pan and a pan cover was pushed over the top. An angled metal arm with adjustable jaws was also fitted on the side of the plate and pivoted so that it could be swung forwards and the edge would rest on the edge of the wheel, or on the pan cover if this was closed. As the trigger was pressed the sear was disconnected and the pressure of the spring forced the wheel to rotate; at the same time the pan cover had to be pushed clear and the grooved edge of the wheel rubbed against the end of the pyrites. This friction generated sparks which fell directly into the priming powder, and this then fired the main charge.

The wheellock offered advantages and it enabled the gunner to do something which was impossible with the matchlock. The weapon could be loaded, spanned and then left ready for instant action without any further attention or care; all that was required to fire it was pressure on the trigger. It also offered greater safety, for if the angled arm, known as the doghead, was lifted clear of the pan, even if the trigger was pressed and the wheel rotated, no sparks were produced since there was no contact with the pyrites and the weapon would not fire.

The origin of the wheellock is obscure. It is possible that it was an Italian invention; certainly Leonardo da Vinci (1452–1519) illustrated

two practical wheellock mechanisms in one of his manuscripts. There are references early in the fifteenth century to 'self-igniting' locks, the context of which would suggest that these were some form of wheellock. However, once the idea had been developed, knowledge of it spread and soon gunmakers throughout Italy and Germany were producing wheellock weapons.

The wheellock was not without its problems: the two main drawbacks stemmed from its complexity, for the old matchlock could have been made and maintained by any metal-working smith. The wheellock could not; it required a degree of skill beyond the abilities of the village blacksmith, and should a fault develop it could not be easily and quickly repaired, with the result that the weapon was probably rendered totally useless. With the matchlock, if the arm or spring broke the weapon could still be fired by the match ready to hand, but with the wheellock this was not possible. The complexity of the mechanism also made it expensive to produce, which placed it beyond the reach of ordinary people; consequently, as a military weapon, it never achieved the widespread use enjoyed by the matchlock.

The wheellock had a working life ranging from the beginning of the sixteenth century through, at least, until the end of the seventeenth century, but gunsmiths were constantly looking for cheaper and simpler mechanisms. The flint-and-

Right

Rare example of a sixteenth-century English musket. The shape of the butt is very similar to that of the older wheellock, and behind the cock is the dog, or hooked catch, to hold it in the safe position.

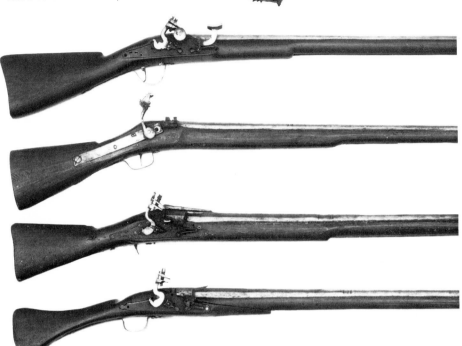

Left

Weapons in an age of transition. *From top to bottom.*
English snaphaunce *c* 1650 bearing the marks of the Ordnance of Commonwealth (1649–66). Matchlock musket with an unusual lock which displays the Gunmaker's Company proof marks. English matchlock dated 1576 but converted to a flintlock around the middle of the seventeenth century. Early flintlock musket with marks of the Blacksmith's Company. The lock is of the early form, the sear engaging with the toe of the cock.

Below right

The cock (1) is pulled back, automatically rotating the tumbler (2). The tip of the sear (3) is pressed against the tumbler and engages with the first notch (4). In this half-cock notch the trigger (5) cannot disengage the sear. If the cock is pulled further back, the sear engages with the second notch (6), the full cock. Pressure on the trigger (5) can now disengage the sear, allowing the mainspring (7), compressed by the tumbler's rotation, to press down on the tip of the tumbler, thus swinging the cock (1) forward. The combined steel and pan cover, the frizzen (8), is struck by the flint, producing sparks and tilting to uncover the pan (9) so that the priming is ignited. The tumbler is secured by the bridle (10), which is screwed to the lockplate (11).

steel method of making fire was very old and was known and used throughout Europe. In northern Europe, bordering the Baltic, a very simple spark-producing mechanism had been evolved based on the traditional flint and steel. A long, slim, metal arm held a chip of flint, a mineral widely distributed throughout Europe. This arm was powered by a simple spring mechanism. If the arm was lifted the spring was compressed and the arm was held under tension in this position. An upright steel plate

Below left

The cock (1) is pulled back, causing the tumbler (2) to rotate. Simultaneously, the nose of the combined sear and trigger lever (3), which passes through a hole (4) in the lockplate, engages with the heel of the cock (1) and locks it in position. The steel (5) is placed vertically in front of the pan (6), and the pan cover (7) is pushed back to cover the priming. When the trigger is pressed, the sear (3) pivots backwards, disengaging the nose from the cock. The mainspring (8), compressed via the tumbler by the movement of the cock, now presses down on the tip of the tumbler, forcing the cock forward. The flint scrapes down the steel making sparks and knocking it clear. The arm (9) moves forward, causing the pan cover to be displaced and the sparks ignite the priming.

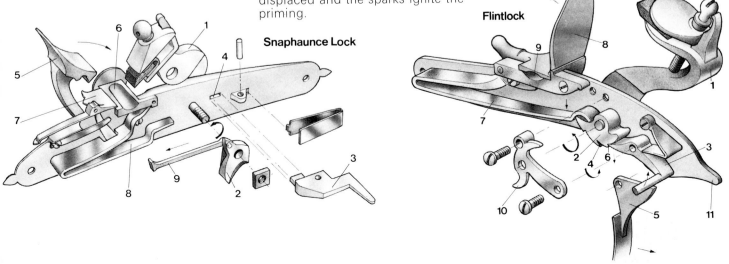

Snaphaunce Lock

Flintlock

was fitted just in front of the pan and when the trigger was pressed, the arm holding the piece of flint swung forward. During part of its traverse it scraped down the steel plate and, as with the wheellock, the friction produced a shower of sparks which fell directly into the priming to discharge the shot.

This so-called Baltic lock was simple, effective and, above all, cheap to produce. To protect the priming powder in the pan a cover was fitted, and this made for a slight complication since the pan cover had to be removed before the sparks were struck. On some Baltic locks this was done manually but on others the pan cover was connected, via internal levers, to the arm holding the flint; as the arm moved forward the pan cover was automatically pushed clear. This system was the snaphaunce, the basis for an ignition

mechanism which was to remain standard for some two and a half centuries. The separate pan cover was a somewhat unnecessary complication, and as early as the sixteenth century a simpler but effective system had been evolved by uniting the steel striking plate and the pan cover into a single L-shaped piece of metal pivoted at the tip of the short arm. This combined arm was so placed that the short arm of the L rested on top of the pan, so serving as the pan cover. The longer, vertical arm served as the striking plate, and this L-shaped piece of metal is generally known today as the frizzen. It was held firmly closed over the pan by the tension of a small V-shaped frizzen spring. When the arm holding the flint, the cock, swung forward and scraped the flint down the plate, the effect was twofold; first sparks were produced and at the same time

the pressure forced the frizzen to pivot forward to uncover the pan, so allowing the sparks to fall into the priming. This simple device was known as the flintlock.

During the sixteenth century and the early part of the seventeenth, all three systems of ignition were in use, matchlock, wheellock and flintlock. Sometime in the first decade of the seventeenth century a Frenchman, Marin le Bourgeoys, a Royal gunmaker in Paris, developed the French lock. This was a form of the flintlock which brought together a number of features already in use on separate locks, and it became the standard ignition mechanism for certainly the next two hundred years.

Most early flintlock and snaphaunce mechanisms operated on a mechanical system very similar to that of the wheellock. When the cock was pulled back a spring-operated arm, the sear, situated on the inside of the lock plate and under pressure from a spring, passed horizontally through a hole in the lockplate and engaged with the cock so locking it into position. When the trigger was pressed then this arm was withdrawn and the cock was allowed to swing forward. This horizontally operating sear made for complications both in design and construction. Le Bourgeoys adopted an idea already a feature of some firearms, and used a vertical sear operating on the inside of the lockplate. He fitted the cock to a squared axle which passed through a hole to the inside of the lock and was united with a shaped

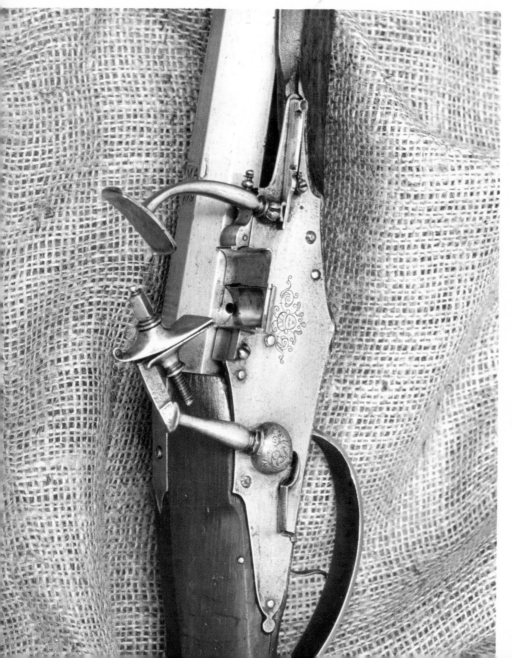

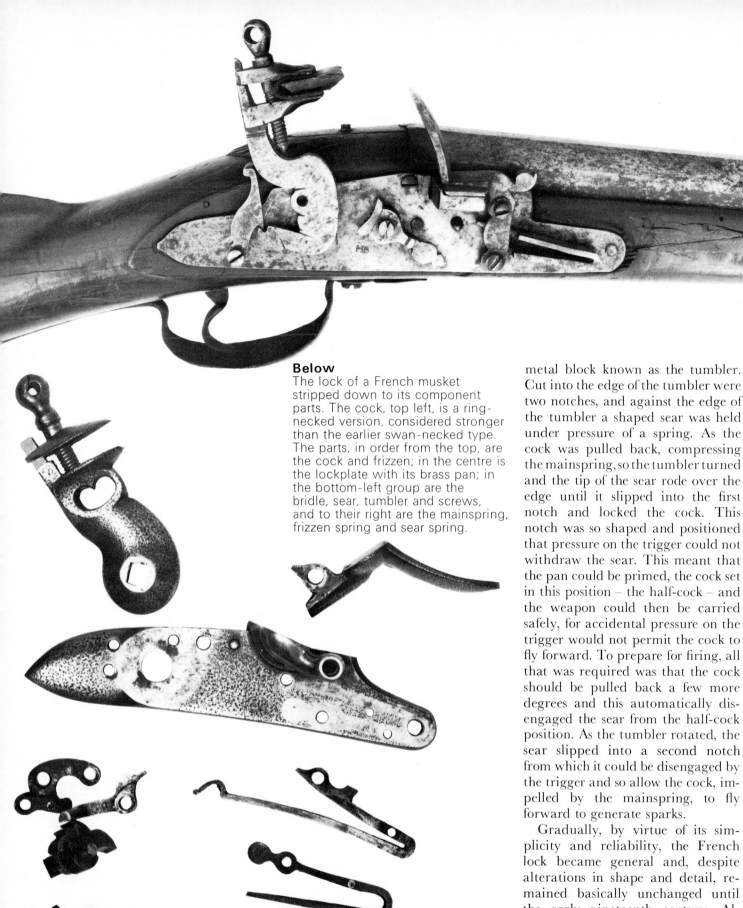

Below
The lock of a French musket stripped down to its component parts. The cock, top left, is a ring-necked version, considered stronger than the earlier swan-necked type. The parts, in order from the top, are the cock and frizzen; in the centre is the lockplate with its brass pan; in the bottom-left group are the bridle, sear, tumbler and screws, and to their right are the mainspring, frizzen spring and sear spring.

metal block known as the tumbler. Cut into the edge of the tumbler were two notches, and against the edge of the tumbler a shaped sear was held under pressure of a spring. As the cock was pulled back, compressing the mainspring, so the tumbler turned and the tip of the sear rode over the edge until it slipped into the first notch and locked the cock. This notch was so shaped and positioned that pressure on the trigger could not withdraw the sear. This meant that the pan could be primed, the cock set in this position – the half-cock – and the weapon could then be carried safely, for accidental pressure on the trigger would not permit the cock to fly forward. To prepare for firing, all that was required was that the cock should be pulled back a few more degrees and this automatically disengaged the sear from the half-cock position. As the tumbler rotated, the sear slipped into a second notch from which it could be disengaged by the trigger and so allow the cock, impelled by the mainspring, to fly forward to generate sparks.

Gradually, by virtue of its simplicity and reliability, the French lock became general and, despite alterations in shape and detail, remained basically unchanged until the early nineteenth century. Although for military and general purposes the flintlock became standard, the wheellock was not completely abandoned and continued to be used on fine-quality pieces until the early eighteenth century. For the

Left
Dog lock from an English musket of *circa* 1650. The lock is of the early type with a long tail to the cock and a metal buffer just below the pan to stop the cock swinging too far forward. W. Keith Neal, Guernsey.

Below
From top to bottom.
Mid-seventeenth-century musket with an early form of flintlock. Unusual English wheellock musket which carries the mark of the Blacksmith's Company of London and is numbered 'XII' on the butt. Dutch signal flintlock gun with brass barrel, dating from the late eighteenth century.

wealthy sportsman who wished to display his riches, the wheellock rifle offered good opportunities. The stock, usually of walnut, was gracefully shaped and inlaid with horn, ivory, mother-of-pearl or steel, and ornamented with restrained carving. The lockplate was frequently chiselled with classical and military motifs and the cock was often shaped as a dragon or other fanciful figure. The barrel, usually octagonal, was sometimes decorated.

Many of these hunting weapons were fitted with a 'set' or hair trigger. This was a device which enabled the firer to discharge the shot with an absolute minimum of pressure on the trigger. This feature remained in use on many later weapons for target shooting, hunting and duelling. The wheellock butt was shaped so that the weapon was held, not against the shoulder, but against the cheek. The kick of the explosion, the recoil, was greatly reduced by the very heavy barrel. By the beginning of the eighteenth century this fashion was abandoned and the wheellock's working life was virtually over.

Although there were minor improvements to the mechanisms of the flintlock it remained virtually unchanged in principle until the 1820s and '30s. During this long period there were changes in style and design. Early flintlocks were mostly fitted with a flat lockplate which had a somewhat characteristic droop at the rear, suggesting a banana shape, but this style was gradually modified from early in the eighteenth century. The old flat lock shape was straightened out and became convex in section. From the latter part of the eighteenth century and the early part of the nineteenth, the lockplate was once again made flat. About the same period the rather graceful swan's neck-shaped cock was replaced by a ring neck which was more rugged in construction. The French military gunmakers had introduced these early in the eighteenth century but they did not appear on British military firearms until the early nineteenth century. The cock was also once again made flat rather than in the convex style popular during the eighteenth century.

The wheellock had been generally reliable but had suffered from the disadvantages of being rather expensive and difficult to maintain. The flintlock was simple to maintain and reliable, but its big advantage was its cheapness. From the end of the seventeenth century onwards

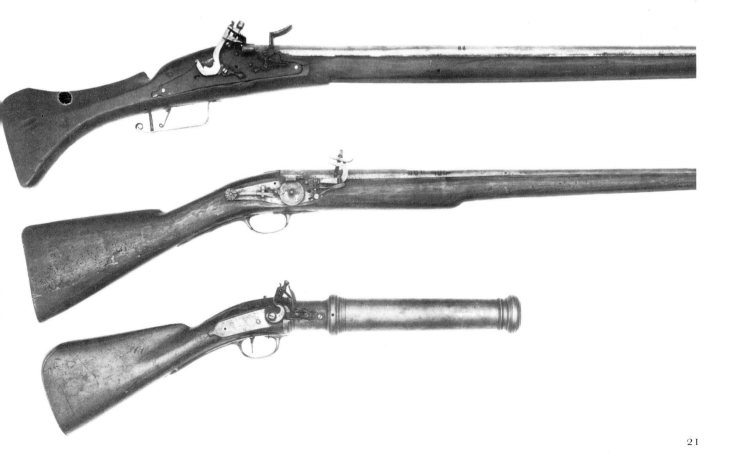

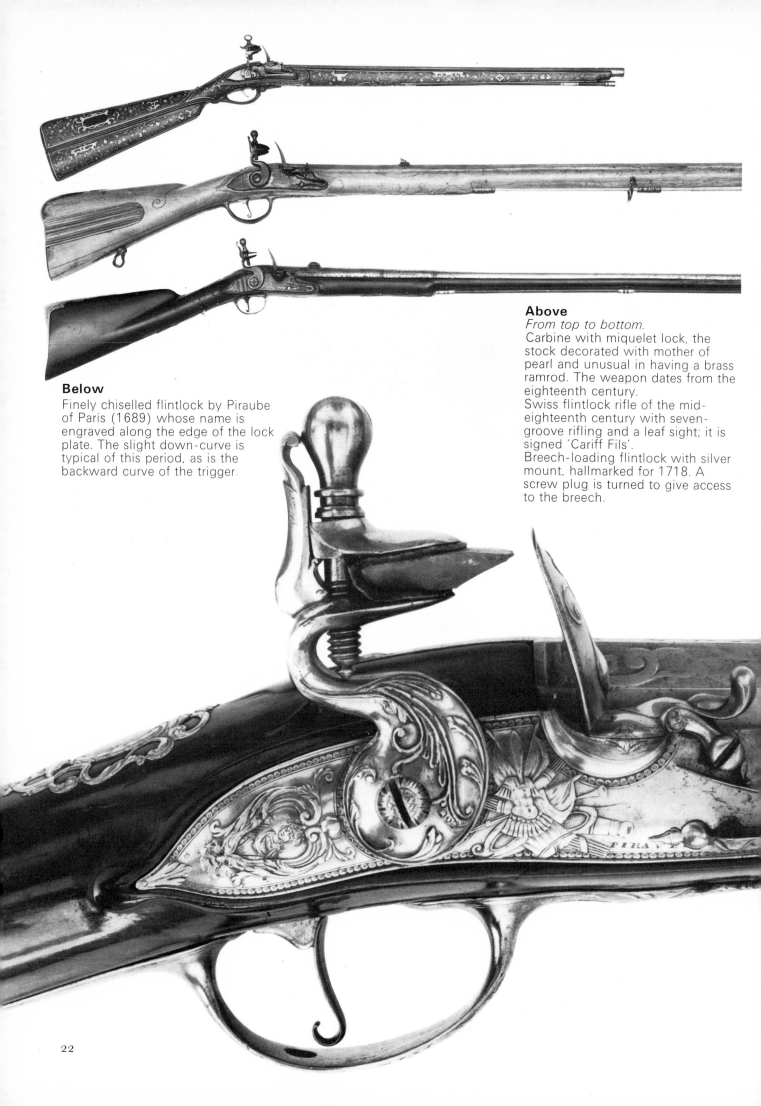

Above
From top to bottom.
Carbine with miquelet lock, the stock decorated with mother of pearl and unusual in having a brass ramrod. The weapon dates from the eighteenth century.
Swiss flintlock rifle of the mid-eighteenth century with seven-groove rifling and a leaf sight; it is signed 'Cariff Fils'.
Breech-loading flintlock with silver mount, hallmarked for 1718. A screw plug is turned to give access to the breech.

Below
Finely chiselled flintlock by Piraube of Paris (1689) whose name is engraved along the edge of the lock plate. The slight down-curve is typical of this period, as is the backward curve of the trigger.

Above
Nelson falls to the deck of his flagship, H.M.S. *Victory*, at the Battle of Trafalgar in 1805, hit in the back by a ball from the musket of a French sharpshooter.
National Maritime Museum, Greenwich.

military firearms were increasingly fitted with this new system of ignition. By the early eighteenth century matchlocks, wheellocks and the snaphaunce had been largely forgotten. Despite its great advantages, however, the flintlock itself was not without its problems and limitations. The flint had only a limited life and it was generally thought that about 30 strikes was the most that could reasonably be expected from a good flint. Some failed to function efficiently after 5–10 shots and others continued working happily for 50 or 60 strikes. This uncertainty meant that the sportsman and the military man had to carry spare flints.

Even more annoying for the sportsman was the phenomenon known as hangfire. This was a delay between the time of pressing the trigger and the discharge of the shot. Each mechanical and chemical operation

Page from an eighteenth-century illustrated French dictionary showing some of the movements in arms drill using the flintlock musket.

priming, a flash and a puff of grey-white smoke. For the military man the smoke was a hindrance in that it tended to obscure his view, but the hangfire was of little importance. Volley fire was the standard military practice of the time and this delay made little or no difference to its effect. But for the sportsman both hangfire and flash were a considerable annoyance. The flash and smoke from the priming gave his quarry a small but, nevertheless, valuable warning that the shot was on its way, and startled the animal or bird into precipitous movement. The hang-fire was also of great importance when the firer was aiming to take a moving target, for he had to make allowance for it by aiming ahead of or above his target.

It fell to a man of many parts, a somewhat obscure cleric in Belhelvie, Aberdeenshire, on the east coast of Scotland to solve these problems. Alexander Forsyth, in addition to his clerical duties, was a keen shot and an amateur scientist. He suffered as much as any hunter from the annoyance of hangfire and priming flash and he sought means to speed up the explosion so that the effects of both were greatly reduced. In order to do this he experimented with chemicals known as fulminates, which were notoriously unstable for even a slight knock could cause them to explode. Forsyth reasoned that if he mixed them with the propellant, the explosion would be speeded up, hang-fire reduced and the warning time given by the flash would be likewise reduced. The experiments were not very successful but Forsyth perceived an alternative approach to the problem. On explosion these fulminates produced a not inconsiderable flash; if their detonation could be controlled, that flash might be used to ignite the charge. He evolved a little gadget known to collectors as the scent bottle, a name derived not from its perfume but from its shape. It was a wide-waisted, metal container the top end of which was solid except for a spring-operated plunger which passed through this section. The lower section of the scent bottle was a small container which held a quantity of fulminate. The scent bottle

took a small, but finite amount of time. As the trigger was pressed the sear was withdrawn; the cock moved forward and struck sparks; the frizzen moved forward; the sparks fell into the pan; the priming flared; the flash passed through the touch-hole; the main charge began to burn, and eventually the bullet was ejected from the barrel. Each of these tiny delays added up to a small but appreciable period – the hangfire. During this period and slightly preceding the shot, there was, from the was pivoted on a metal block through which was drilled a small tunnel connecting with the touch-hole. The scent bottle was rotated about the central block and this allowed a few grains of the fulminate to fall out into the channel adjacent to the touch-hole. The scent bottle was now returned to its original position so that the spring-operated striker was above these grains of fulminate.

The internal mechanism of the lock was unaltered but the cock was replaced by a solid-nosed hammer. When the trigger was pressed the hammer swung forward and struck the plunger, which was pushed down to strike the grains of fulminate. The flash from the explosion passed through the touch-hole to ignite the main charge. Forsyth found that he had built a practical ignition system which had the added advantage that it was not too difficult to adapt a flintlock weapon to take this new method. The new system was known as the percussion lock, since detonation was produced by the striking of a hammer.

Forsyth patented his method in 1807 and was encouraged to contact the Master-General of the Ordnance, who was responsible for the supply of arms and ammunition to all British

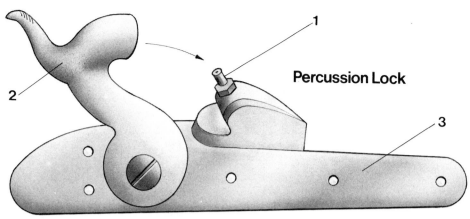

Percussion Lock

forces. This he did, was invited to London and given facilities for research and development in the Tower of London. All did not go as well as Forsyth might have expected, and then there was a change of Master-General. The new man was not impressed by Forsyth's work and more or less bundled him out of the Tower. Forsyth set up a shop at No 10 Piccadilly, London, and sold guns and pistols fitted with his scent bottle.

His patent was well drawn up, and other gunmakers who attempted to copy his system found themselves in legal trouble. However, alternative systems of depositing the fulminate in the touch-hole were developed by many gunsmiths. Fulminate was supplied in small tubes of metal foil, in small hollow quills, as pills of

Above
A percussion cap is placed over the small metal pillar, the nipple (1). The hammer (2) is pulled back to the full-cock position and the internal mechanism operates in exactly the same manner as on the flintlock. When the trigger is pressed, the hammer (2) falls forward to strike the cap on the nipple so achieving detonation. The nipple is attached to the barrel and not the lockplate (3).

Below
To overcome the problem of size there were many attempts to produce pistols which could serve as carbines. This officer's double-barrelled pistol was made c 1815 by Staudenmayer of London. The shoulder stock clips on to the butt.

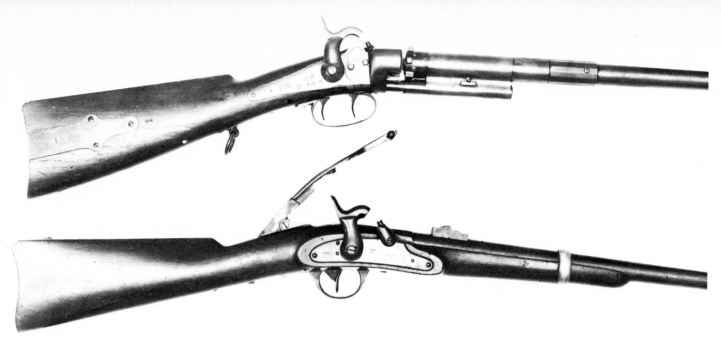

powder held together with various adhesives, and even in small paper caps reminiscent of those used by children. These various receptacles were positioned by the touch-hole to be hit by some form of hammer.

All these containers suffered from one great disadvantage: they were so small that their handling was difficult. In conditions of war or on the sporting field, where wind, rain and gloves might further hamper movement, they were almost impossible to use efficiently. The solution to this problem came around 1815–20 when the percussion cap was developed. It consisted of a small copper thimble, and on the inside of the top was deposited a small quantity of fulminate. The cap could be pushed over the end of a small metal pillar, known as the nipple, through which a hole had been drilled to connect with the touch-hole. It was usually a push-fit, held in place by friction, but

on some military weapons it was secured by a small metal arm. The hammer swung forward and forced the cap down on the top of the nipple, and the collision detonated the fulminate to produce a flash which ignited the main charge. The identity of the inventor of the percussion cap has never been finally settled, and a number of famous gunmakers of the time laid claim to this honour. On balance it would seem that the credit should go to a British artist who had emigrated to America, Joshua Shaw. Whoever invented it,

the cap was a sound, practical device and it was adopted for all manner of locks, and was to continue in use until well into the 1860s and '70s before it was finally displaced by metal centre-fire cartridges.

The other great innovation of the nineteenth century which so improved the performance of firearms was the widespread adoption of rifling. When a lead ball was driven along the barrel by the force of the

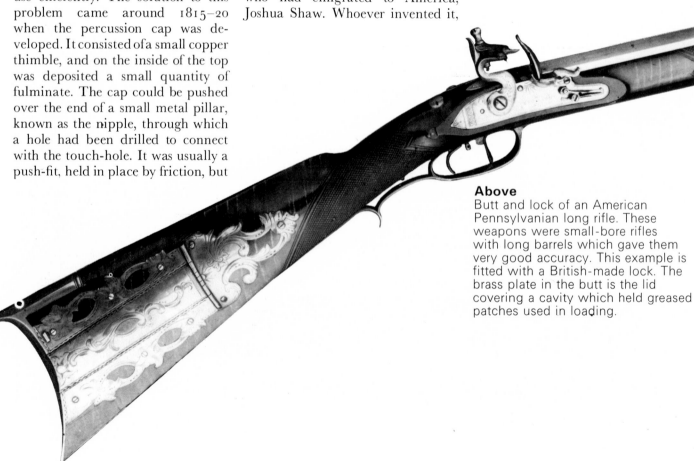

Above
Butt and lock of an American Pennsylvanian long rifle. These weapons were small-bore rifles with long barrels which gave them very good accuracy. This example is fitted with a British-made lock. The brass plate in the butt is the lid covering a cavity which held greased patches used in loading.

Left
Top. The American-designed Greene breech-loader carbine of 1856, fitted with a Maynard tape-capping lock. The barrel was pivoted and swung forward to permit the loading of the cartridges.
Bottom. Merrill carbine — an early form of breech-loader; the breech was opened by lever, and cartridges were loaded directly into it.

Below
Finely engraved percussion lock from a 16-bore, two-groove rifle made by the London gunmaker Charles Lancaster in 1853 for the Maharajah of Jodhpur. It is fitted with a sliding-bolt safety catch and a platinum vent at the base of the nipple.

exploding gunpowder it bounced from side to side. The amount of bounce was very small indeed, but as the ball left the muzzle some part of its surface was more firmly in contact with the inside of the barrel than the rest. This produced a slight degree of drag or friction sufficient to produce a minute deflection from the true flight-line of the bullet. The last point of contact between bullet and barrel could vary for each shot, and the bullet was deflected slightly in any one of several directions entirely as a matter of chance. If the ball was made to fit very tightly inside the barrel to reduce the 'bounce' then a new problem developed, since the ball became extremely difficult to load.

The shape of the bullet also affected the trajectory: any slight irregularities in shape, such as bubbles left during the casting, disturbed its balance and its line of flight. The solution lay in reducing all these variants as much as possible so that the direction was constant. If the bullet could be made to spin about its axis, the variations in direction could be cancelled out. Any tendency to veer because of a variation in size or weight was immediately nullified, since the effect of the imperfection was spread equally in all directions. The corrective influence of spin had been known from the earliest times, and some arrows were made with the vanes adjusted to give the arrow a spinning motion.

The problem facing the gunsmiths was how to achieve this spin, and the answer lay in the use of rifling, that is, in cutting a number of parallel, shallow, spiral grooves on the inside surface of the barrel. The raised ridges between the grooves, the lands, bit into the bullet and forced it to follow the line of the grooves along the barrel so that as the bullet left the muzzle it was spinning about its axis. The amount of spin was determined by the twist of the grooves, and there was much argument as to the ideal pitch, width, depth and number of grooves, and most gunmakers made their own choice. All these facts had long been known but their application had been limited by practical problems, for it had been difficult to

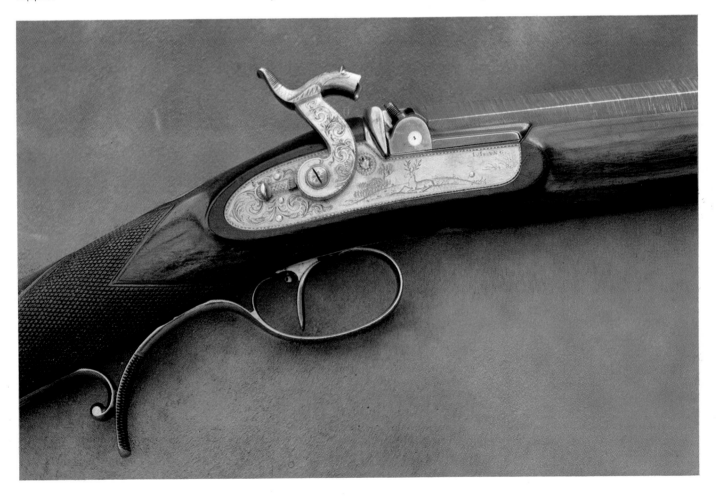

cut the grooves on the inside of the barrel using available technology. It required a great deal of skill and time. Many of the wheellock sporting guns were rifled and capable of a high degree of accuracy, but these were expensive weapons. Rifles for military use were not readily available because of the expense and difficulties of production. Hunting rifles were produced, the famous American Pennsylvanian long rifle being a notable example. These owed their development to the influx of German gunsmiths who were familiar with the Jäger hunting rifle. The Jäger was a rather shorter, heavier weapon whilst the American one had a small bore, about .4 in (10.2 mm), and a very long barrel. The use of a long barrel ensured that the powder could develop maximum pressure, and that the bullet was given a good spin. It also facilitated

taking a careful aim. British troops during the American War of Independence (1775–83) were to feel the effects of this weapon in the hands of some of the militia and volunteer units of the American forces.

During the nineteenth century, following the Industrial Revolution, powered machinery of all types made manufacturing a much simpler process. Machines were developed capable of mass-producing rifled barrels and from the mid-nineteenth century onwards rifled weapons became commonplace.

In addition to the general adoption of rifles, the most important development in firearms during the middle years of the nineteenth century were the introduction of breech-loading weapons and metal-cased cartridges. Breech-loading had long been the desire of firearms designers, since muzzle-loading was both in-

This photograph taken in February 1905 at Mullah-monsoor Camp in India shows British Regulars still equipped with the .303 Martini-Enfield single-shot rifle over 15 years after the adoption of the bolt-action magazine rifle.

efficient and slow. Tearing open the cartridge, pouring down the powder and ramming home the bullet took time and slowed the rate of fire. If powder and ball could be placed directly into the breech, both time and effort could be saved. As with rifling, the idea was not new: the earliest cannons had been breech-loaders, and the same principle had been tried for hand firearms. A small, separate chamber, loaded with powder and shot, had been fitted against the barrel and the shot was fired, then the empty chamber was replaced by a fully charged one. Unfortunately this system, as did most others, suffered from one great problem which was the loss of gas through the joint between chamber and barrel. The escaping gas was a hazard for the shooter as well as being responsible for a loss in power. This problem of obturating or sealing the breech and preventing gas escape was to dog breech-loading weapons for centuries.

There were several successful attempts to overcome the problem and one of the most notable was that of Captain Patrick Ferguson who, in 1776, designed a breech-loading rifle which operated by a threaded plug which could be lowered by rotating the trigger guard to expose the breech. Powder and ball were fed in, the trigger guard was again turned, so locking the plug back into position, and the weapon was loaded. It proved itself to be an efficient and practical weapon, but for a variety of reasons it was never taken up and developed on a large scale.

Cartridges, too, had been in use from the fifteenth century, and were an improvement over the powder flask or powder horn, which were often decorative items but slow in use and a hindrance to the shooter. One most important step towards solving the problem of obturation and the development of an effective cartridge came about in 1835, when Casimir Lefaucheux, a Frenchman, introduced the pin-fire cartridge. This used a metal case with a small, solid pin projecting from the side at the rear end. The tip of the rod rested against a small quantity of fulminate imbedded in the powder in the cart-ridge. Pin-fire weapons had small slots at the breech or cylinder through which the pin could protrude, and a hammer which struck the pin so detonating the fulminate and firing the charge. They were useful and reliable but they tended to be a little unsafe since it was easy to administer an accidental blow on the protruding pin. Other attempts to improve on the design were made, and people such as the Swiss gunmaker Samuel Johannes Pauly pointed a way.

Pauly's cartridge of 1812 was, in many respects, the same as the modern shotgun cartridge. It consisted of a separate base fitted with its own percussion cap. His guns were also breech-loading. The big break came in 1857 when the American firm of Smith and Wesson acquired a patent by Rollin White for a revolver cylinder with the chambers drilled right through. They had also developed a rim-fire cart-ridge: this was a copper case with a small amount of fulminate deposited internally on the rim which projected beyond the wall of the case. The cartridge was loaded with powder and the ball was inserted in the other end. The cartridge dropped into the chamber until the projecting rim sat on the face of the cylinder; the hammer then struck the rim crushing it against the cylinder, detonating the fulminate and so firing the bullet. The system proved totally successful although there were problems in developing large-calibre rim-fire cartridges. In order to provide enough power to discharge a larger bullet, the charge of propellant had to be increased. The high pressure necessitated a stronger case but this made it difficult to crush the rim to detonate the fulminate. Metal cases were tough and durable and also helped solve the problem of obturation, for as the powder exploded so the metal case of the cart-ridge expanded slightly in the chamber and effectively blocked off all gas escaping to the rear.

Development was now rapid. Henry Daw and Colonel Boxer in Britain and Colonel Berdan in the United States designed metal-cased cartridges with the percussion cap, or primer, set at the centre of the base.

The first cases presented problems for they were made of coiled brass, and proved ineffective; later the cartridge case was pressed out from a single piece of metal, which proved to be far more satisfactory.

The factors involved in the design of a cartridge are many, and much thought has gone into producing cartridges for specific purposes. Bullet weight, shape and size are important; case shape, length and thickness have to be considered, and all these features affect the choice of the propellant and primer. Since the mid-nineteenth century hundreds of rifle and shotgun cartridges have been developed, each claiming some special feature. If any general trend can be detected, it must be the gradual reduction in the size of the military bullet. In Britain the eighteenth-century Brown Bess ball was around .75 in (19.6 mm), the nineteenth-century Enfield rifle was .577 in (14.7 mm), and the twentieth-century Lee-Enfield was .303 in (7.7 mm). Today most of the world's military rifles use a bullet of about 7.62 mm. Incidentally, cartridges are usually defined by their calibre, but they can be found with two sets of figures such as 44-40. This means that .44 in (11.2 mm) is the calibre, but the second figure can stand for a variety of details such as the size of the charge or the length of the case; there is still little standardization in cartridge terminology.

Thus by the late nineteenth century the modern rifle had been developed, and most armies were equipped with magazine weapons. They could be loaded with a number of rounds, and by operating a bolt or lever mechanism fresh cartridges could be fed, in turn, into the breech. Development since then has been largely devoted to improving the features introduced in the nineteenth century. Today the modern rifle can be mass-produced and ammunition has improved enormously, giving both outstanding accuracy and consistency.

Sporting Guns

Richard Whittaker

Handguns, as distinct from cannon, seem to have been introduced to warfare in the second half of the fourteenth century. It is difficult to see why they were used at all. The contemporary longbow and crossbow were far more accurate, and could be fired more quickly, while their armour-piercing capability was little inferior. The advantage of the handgun rested more on its ability to frighten horses, cause, so it was claimed, incurable wounds, and boost the technological status of its deployer, than on any ballistic superiority. But there was another factor close to the hearts of commanders fighting beyond their means – cost. Guns were cheaper than crossbows, and any peasant could be trained in their use in weeks. The years of training necessary for crossbowmen and, especially, longbowmen made them scarce, and increased the cost of employing them as mercenaries.

But the early handgun had no advantages for sporting use, and was not so used until about 1500, by which time it had been considerably improved. The barrel was longer and better bored, the stock had been developed to assist the aim, and the primitive matchlock had replaced the separate slow match of the earlier design. All the same, the gun was still a fine-weather weapon, dirty and inaccurate, and guaranteed to frighten the game for miles around.

Three inventions soon improved the performance of the gun as a sporting weapon – the wheellock, rifling and shot. The wheellock has been described in the last chapter. It simplified stalking by enabling the gun to remain cocked for extended periods without adjustment, and then to be fired quickly and reliably when the trigger was pulled. Its intricacy and consequent high cost, however, restricted its use to better-quality weapons, and the matchlock remained in wide use in Europe until the third quarter of the seventeenth century.

Rifling probably appeared in the first quarter of the sixteenth century, although some authorities put its invention a little earlier, about 1490.

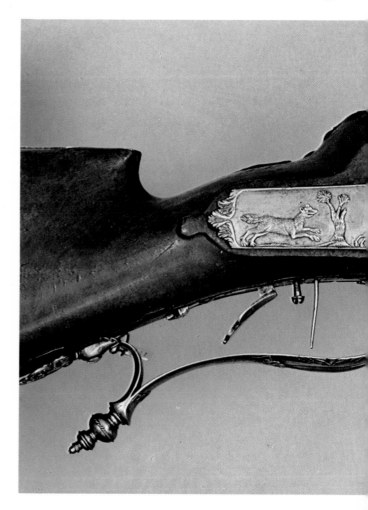

Above
A wheellock gun of the late sixteenth century firing two superimposed charges with two locks. This apparently risky idea was used all through the muzzle-loading period. Tight wads kept the flame of the first charge from igniting the second. Victoria and Albert Museum, London.

Below
The wheellock became an artistic creation as well as a weapon, and the steelwork of this weapon has been elaborately chiselled into grotesque figures. The weapon bears the name of Johann Jacob Bahr of Wurtzburg. Bavarian National Museum, Munich.

A rifled barrel is cut with spiral grooves to impart spin to the bullet. This makes it fire more accurately, any imbalance in the bullet's form or density being cancelled out by the rotation, like that of a spinning top.

It is not certain how it was invented. Arrows and crossbow bolts had long been made to rotate by off-set flights, and it may have been a development of this. It may have been a chance discovery arising from the experimental use of grooves to contain the powder fouling. It was certainly not the result of correct theory practically applied, to judge from the recorded beliefs of its effect. Some were, briefly, that the bullet bored its way through the air like a gimlet, that the tighter fit of the rifle bullet enabled the powder to develop more power, that a rifle bullet had a

higher muzzle velocity than a smooth-bore of identical bore diameter and powder charge, and that the devil could not ride on a spinning ball. All were wrong, although precise proof of the fallacy in the last theory is elusive.

The problem with all muzzle-loading rifles until the invention of expansive bullets in the mid-nineteenth century lay in making the bullet follow the rifling. The bullet, a soft lead sphere, was in contact with the barrel only around a narrow

Right
A light sporting rifle called a *tschinke*, popular in Silesia and Poland where it was used for small-game shooting. Note the tunnel backsight. The wheellock mechanism was mounted externally to make it easier to clean out the fragments of flint or pyrites that fell into it.

SHOOTING FLYING   p: 170

To the Honourable Thomas Fairfax Esqr eldest Son of y^e R^t Hon.^{bl} Henry Lord Fairfax of Denton in York-shire. This Plate is humbly Dedicated by Richard Blome.

Left
English gentlemen of the seventeenth century indulge in their shooting from the saddle. They are accompanied by grooms who, no doubt, loaded the guns, and packs of dogs. W. Keith Neal, Guernsey.

32

equator. This limited contact had to transmit the torque or twisting force necessary to spin the bullet, and this was determined by two main factors. The first of these was the diameter of the bullet: larger balls needed very much more torque. The second was the rate of rotational acceleration – how quickly the ball's speed of rotation was being increased at any instant as it went from the breech to the muzzle; this in turn depended on two more factors – the pitch, or amount of twist, of the rifling, more twist giving more acceleration, and the ball's rate of acceleration up the barrel: the greater it was, the greater also was the rate of rotational acceleration. If the rifling did not have enough hold on the bullet to transmit the torque required, the bullet simply skidded over it, and the rifle shot as a badly bored smooth-bore.

Three ways of loading the rifle were developed to help the rifling grip the bullet. The most common, and probably the earliest, was to wrap the bullet in a greased leather or cloth patch. The bullet was then forced into the muzzle by the rifleman using his thumb or a 'starter' to spread the pressure over his palm. Once entered into the rifling, the bullet was rammed home with a wooden ramrod. It was a simple and effective method, lasting to the end of the muzzle-loading era. The patch acted as a slightly resilient packing between the bullet and the rifling, carried lubricant, and helped to sweep out the powder fouling left by earlier shots. The bullet itself was not deformed except by being slightly impressed with the rifling if it was a tight fit. But all depended on the bullet and patch fitting the barrel fairly exactly, and this fit was quickly upset by the powder fouling.

Fouling occurred because gunpowder – the only propellant in use until the 1880s – burnt to leave about half its weight in gas and half in solid matter. The solid matter that was not expelled with the gases coated the inside of the barrel so quickly, especially in dry weather, that loading could become impossible after fewer than 10 shots. The fouling could be swabbed out with wet rags, but was obviously inconvenient.

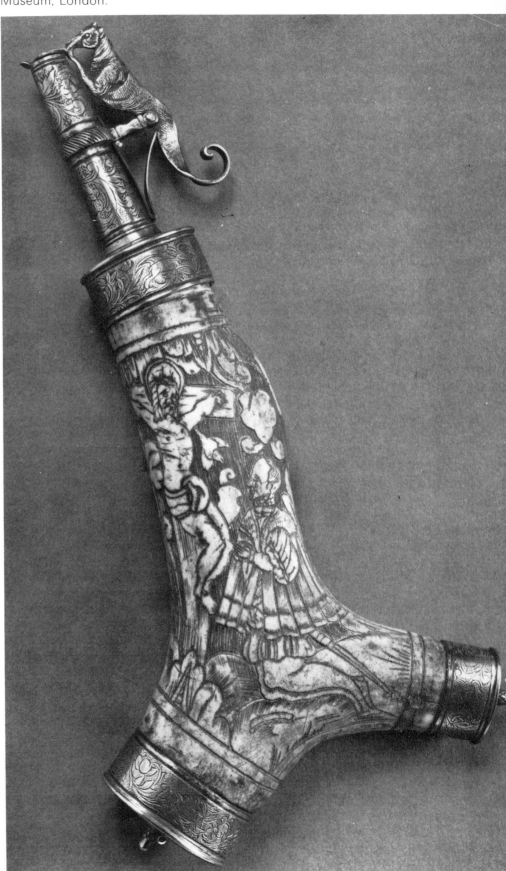

Staghorn powder flask of the late sixteenth century, engraved with a scene showing the conversion of St Hubert. A cut-off is fitted, but there is no measure. Victoria and Albert Museum, London.

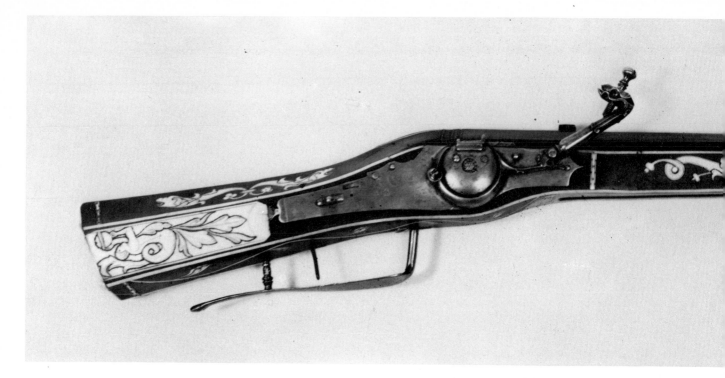

The second method, seldom used for sporting weapons, was to put a ball slightly larger than the bore on to the muzzle, and to hammer it into and down the barrel with a mallet and iron ramrod. While this method gave the rifling an excellent grip on the bullet, the latter was much deformed. Loading was also rather slow.

The third method was to load the rifle at the breech. This was achieved in countless ways, but the commonest were to unscrew the barrel completely, or to have a removable plug. If the breech chamber and bullet were made slightly larger than the bore, the powder had to force the bullet into the barrel when the gun was fired, giving an excellent fit of bullet to rifling. It also ensured that the powder had to develop some pressure before the bullet started, giving higher velocities from shorter barrels. Against the system were its complication, expense and lack of durability, since the high-pressure powder gases forced themselves and gritty fouling into the threads and other finely fitted joints on which the breech sealing depended. No completely gas-tight means of sealing the breech was developed until the mid-nineteenth century.

Shot appeared in the second quarter of the sixteenth century. Instead of a single ball, the gun was loaded

Top
A matchlock gun. Most examples date from the sixteenth and seventeenth centuries. Victoria and Albert Museum, London.

Above
How to shoot ducks: the patch box and butt of a sporting rifle dated 1602.

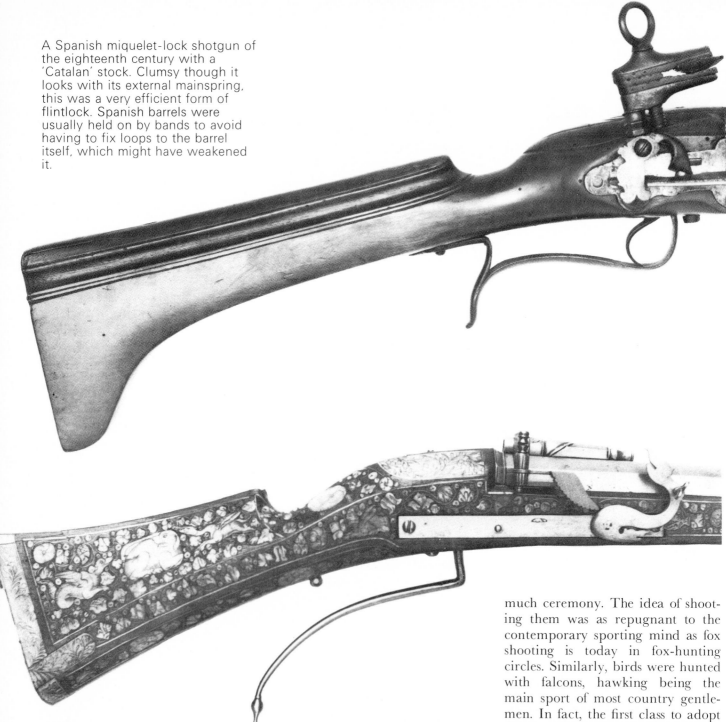

A Spanish miquelet-lock shotgun of the eighteenth century with a 'Catalan' stock. Clumsy though it looks with its external mainspring, this was a very efficient form of flintlock. Spanish barrels were usually held on by bands to avoid having to fix loops to the barrel itself, which might have weakened it.

Sporting matchlock, *circa* 1590, probably of Flemish origin. The stock is ornately worked with inlays of leaves and fanciful animals. It has a lever rather than a trigger to operate the matchlock. Koninklijk Nederlands Leger- en Wapenmuseum 'Generaal Hoefer', Leiden.

with a charge containing a large number of small projectiles.

The shotgun was a bird-killer vastly superior to anything previously used. The rifle was a deadly big-game weapon. But mere technical superiority was not enough to ensure their universal adoption. Other factors obtained.

By the mid-sixteenth century the only dangerous animals in Britain were a few wolves in remote districts. Red deer were the only big game suitable for rifle shooting and these were hunted with hounds amidst much ceremony. The idea of shooting them was as repugnant to the contemporary sporting mind as fox shooting is today in fox-hunting circles. Similarly, birds were hunted with falcons, hawking being the main sport of most country gentlemen. In fact, the first class to adopt the sporting firearm enthusiastically in Britain seems to have been the poor in search of a square meal. Needless to add, numerous laws forbade their owning or using guns of any kind, but they were often disregarded. The guns, as might be expected, were very primitive matchlocks with long barrels of around 5–6 ft (1.5–1.8 m) to judge from contemporary illustrations, and were of moderate bore, around .6–.7 in (15–18 mm). The long barrels were ballistically necessary to give reasonably close shot patterns with the very slow-burning powder of the period.

One matchlock and three wheellock petronels, all fitted with the French style of stock. This type of weapon was fired with the butt held against the chest.

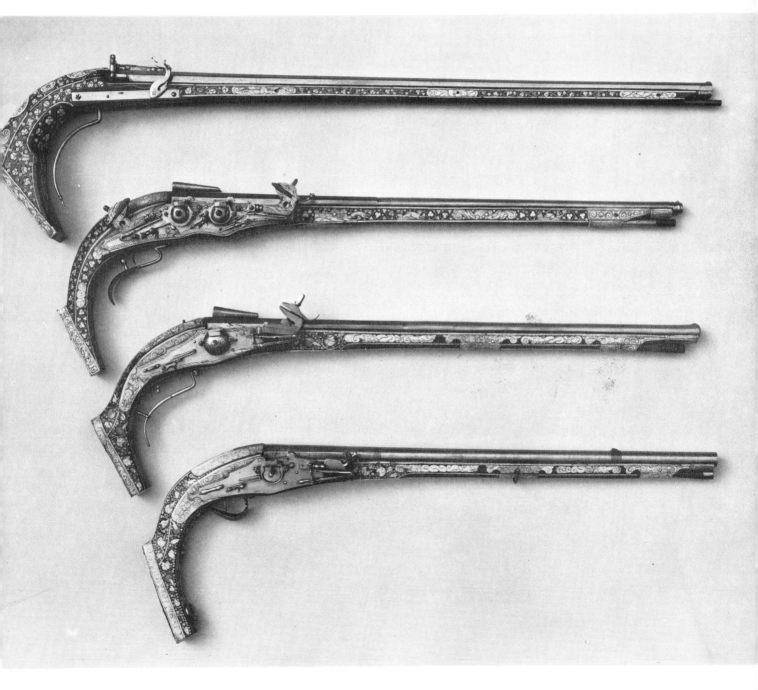

Above
A very good-quality flintlock
sporting rifle made by P. Poser of
Prague *c* 1750. Despite its elaborate
decoration this rifle is still functional,
but it is doubtful whether all such
weapons were intended for serious
use. W. Keith Neal, Guernsey.

Right
This fine-quality, Austrian flintlock
rifle (*circa* 1740) has the rather
thick stock and wooden cover to the
butt patch-box common on
European weapons. The lock is
decorated with applied and
chiselled brass. Terence Porter,
Milton Keynes.

The shotgun was held in like low esteem on the Continent, but not so the rifle, and with good reason. The forests contained big game of many kinds including bears, wolves and wild boar. Many of them were very dangerous. The hunting weapons in common use were the spear and the crossbow. The rifle was an obvious replacement for the crossbow, and involved no great change in the hunting technique. It was widely adopted by all classes – and surprisingly quickly considering that a new technology had to be developed and disseminated.

Continental sporting rifles of the sixteenth and early seventeenth centuries developed along practical lines. Typically, they weighed 8–10 lb (3.6–4.5 kg) and had barrels 2½–3 ft (76–91 cm) long. They were usually under .65-in (16.57-mm) bore with rifling making one revolution in about 6 ft (1.82 m), although this varied widely. The moderate bore and gradual rifling twist were well suited to the use of patched balls, as the risk of stripping, when the bullet simply rode over the grooves, was reduced. Sometimes a wad was put behind the bullet to help to seal the bore and sweep out the fouling. The poor powder also helped to reduce the risk of stripping, as the large charges of slow burning powder used gave a steady acceleration from

breech to muzzle, even though this probably produced considerable muzzle flash. Muzzle velocities were low, at most about 800–900 ft per second (244–274 metres per second). The disadvantage of patched balls – the difficulty of loading them after a few shots – was not important in hunting where very few shots were fired in the day, and there was ample time for cleaning. The Continental custom of driven game and mass slaughter came later.

The stocks of the early guns and rifles were of three types. The French type, or so it was described in a discourse of 1590, was very curved and was butted against the chest. It died out at the end of the sixteenth century. The present-day type, or, rather, its angular ancestor, was described in the same 'discourse' as being of Spanish origin. Many rifles of a third type were made until the middle of the seventeenth century with very short butts, often with a knob at the rear extremity. These were apparently simply placed against the cheek – proof of the low muzzle velocities then current, since such an arrangement would have been impossible had the weapon recoiled with any force.

Smooth-bores firing a single ball, universally used as military weapons, were also evidently employed for sporting purposes, since many

surviving examples are too decorated for military use. They were probably used for short-range game shooting up to about 50 yd (45 m), where speed of loading was more important than accuracy.

English-made rifles, as opposed to imported Continental ones, appeared in the mid-seventeenth century in very small numbers. Almost all seem to have been breech-loaders. They were probably intended for deer shooting when it was impossible to pursue the quarry on horseback; in such conditions a powerful and accurate long-range first shot following a stalk was of more importance than speed of loading. As it happened, they made excellent sniping rifles in the English Civil War, although this can hardly be described as sporting use. All English sporting rifles of the seventeenth and eighteenth centuries were expensive, high-quality arms, unlike Continental rifles which, though always functional, reflected the varying affluence of their owners. It must be remembered that firearms until about 1850 were made by skilled craftsmen, using laborious and slow hand methods. All firearms, especially rifles, represented many man hours of expensive work, and must often have been their owner's most valuable possession.

As time went on the shotgun be-

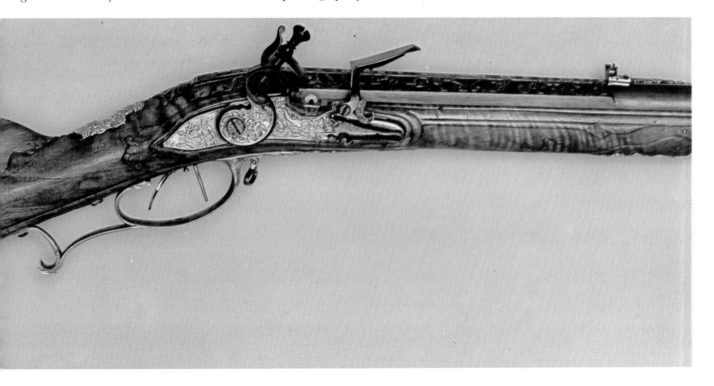

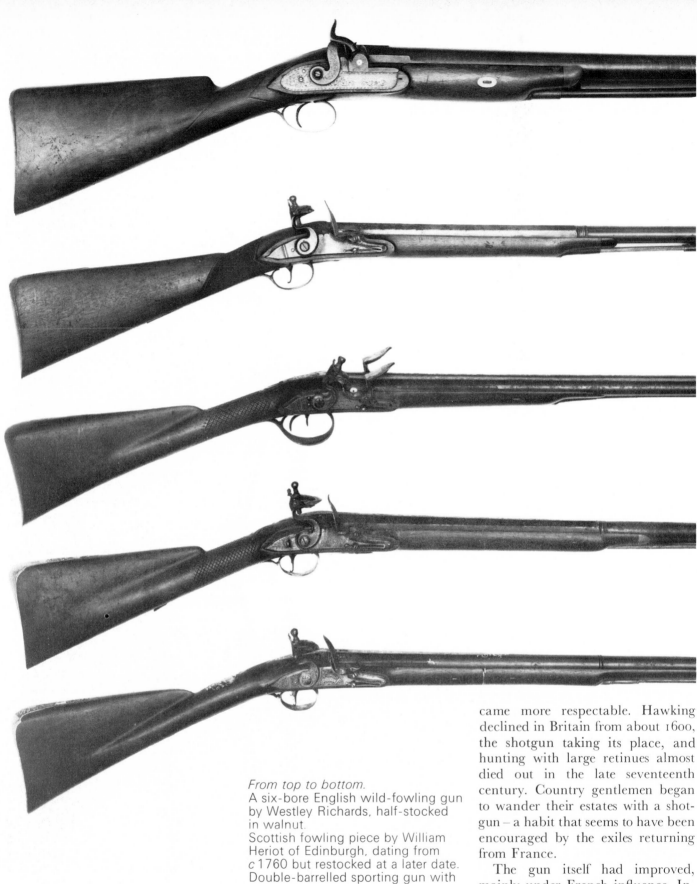

From top to bottom.
A six-bore English wild-fowling gun
by Westley Richards, half-stocked
in walnut.
Scottish fowling piece by William
Heriot of Edinburgh, dating from
c 1760 but restocked at a later date.
Double-barrelled sporting gun with
French-made barrels and English
locks.
Gun with Spanish-type barrel
and silver mounts with hallmarks
for 1763; the lock is by W. Bailes
of London.
Similar gun with silver mounts,
hallmarked for 1764. The locks are
by Hadley of London.

came more respectable. Hawking
declined in Britain from about 1600,
the shotgun taking its place, and
hunting with large retinues almost
died out in the late seventeenth
century. Country gentlemen began
to wander their estates with a shotgun – a habit that seems to have been
encouraged by the exiles returning
from France.

The gun itself had improved,
mainly under French influence. Indeed, some French craftsmen came
to England at the time of the Restoration. With improved gunpowder
the barrel length had been reduced
to about 40 in (1 m), and with the
gunsmiths' improved skills the whole
weapon became lighter and more

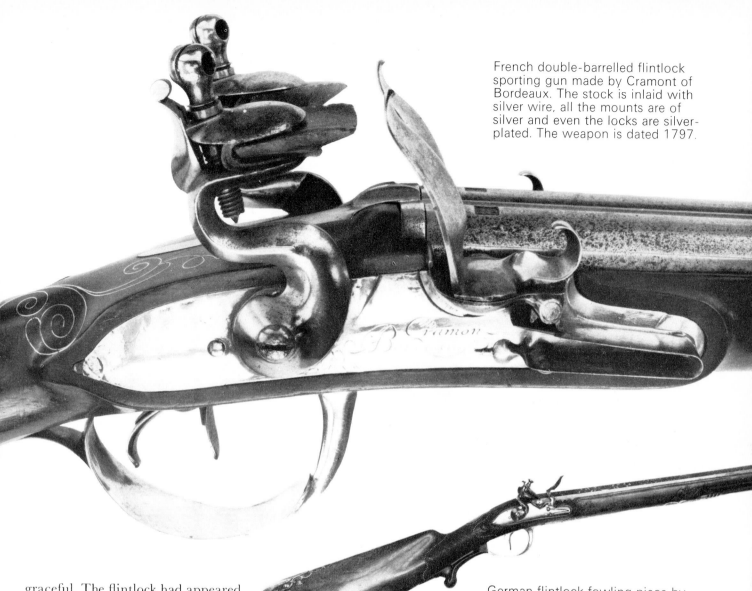

French double-barrelled flintlock sporting gun made by Cramont of Bordeaux. The stock is inlaid with silver wire, all the mounts are of silver and even the locks are silver-plated. The weapon is dated 1797.

German flintlock fowling piece by Chretien Koerber A Ingelfingen. The octagonal barrel has applied silver oak leaves, and the stock is inlaid with ebony and silver studs. The carving on the butt behind the trigger is a common feature of European guns.

graceful. The flintlock had appeared early in the seventeenth century, and was in general use by 1660. A custom also introduced, or at least described, by the returning exiles was that of shooting birds flying, but this was not the usual practice until the late eighteenth century. Before that date, all game was shot sitting.

The late seventeenth century and the first three-quarters of the eighteenth were not marked by any notable advances in shotgun design, but rather by steady improvement. Locks were better fitted. Barrels were better bored. Many shotguns of this period have barrels which flare out towards the muzzle, which apparently improved the shot pattern, although it is difficult to see why. This style of boring probably originated in Spain, where the art of shotgun barrel making had been raised to a very high level.

Barrels could be either forged or cast, but cast barrels were almost useless because of their weight and lack of strength. After about 1550 they were used only for blunderbusses, for which a short thick barrel of brass was not too heavy, and had the further advantage that it did not rust. Thick though they were, however, blunderbuss barrels often burst.

Most barrels were forged. The earliest method was to take a strip of iron a little longer than the barrel and a little wider than its circumference. Heated red hot, it was first made into a long trough shape. It was then bent over a rod and forge-welded inch by inch into a tube. This tube was reamed out internally by passing larger and larger drilling bits through it until a smooth fault-free surface was obtained of about the required diameter. Fine boring was carried out with cutters taking very

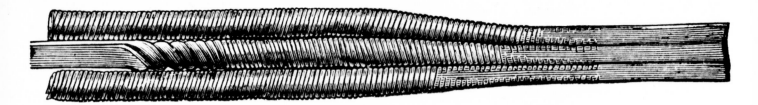

Types of twist barrel. The number of strands and the twist given to them gave the barrel its 'figure' when etched with mild acid.

shallow cuts to finish the barrel. Rifling was formed by pulling cutting bits through the barrel using primitive guides to give the twist. The outside of the barrel was shaped by grinding and filing, great skill being required to keep the outside and inside surfaces concentric, and so ensuring that the barrel wall was of a constant thickness. No great effort was made to bore the barrel to any precise diameter. It was far more important to have a smooth interior, or, in the case of the rifle, a bore diameter that was the same from breech to muzzle with parallel rifling grooves.

Once made, the bore diameter could be specified, if required, by a simple method still used in Britain for shotguns. The 'bore' was equal to the number of identical solid lead spheres, any of which would approximately fit the bore, that made 1 lb weight. Thus, for example, a 16-bore gun took a 1-oz ball, there being 16 oz to the pound. Obviously, the diameter was not specified very exactly. Gunmakers never, for instance, used halves in bore sizes. But until the advent of standardized ammunition, it did not matter. The shotgun owner found by experiment the powder charge and shot load that suited his shotgun. Similarly the rifle owner found the powder charge, patching and bullet that suited his rifle.

The Spanish introduced improvements. Instead of making the barrel in one piece, they made five or six short tubes which were then forged together. Spanish barrels were exported to many European countries in the first half of the eighteenth century. Their popularity in Britain fell in the second half of the century as the British became better barrel makers themselves. In particular, the British became experts in making twist barrels. In this method of manufacture a thin ribbon of iron $\frac{1}{4}$–$\frac{1}{2}$ in (6.35–12.7 mm) wide was wound closely round an iron rod like a corkscrew and was then forged into a solid tube. In this way the grain of the iron was best disposed to resist the pressure of the exploding gunpowder, and the barrel could be made both light and strong. The art of making twist barrels was well known to the Turks in the seventeenth century, and Turkish barrels, often rifled, are found on English and Continental weapons. A great many had been captured during the fighting which occurred when the Turks besieged Vienna in 1683.

Another invention of great importance to the shotgun was the

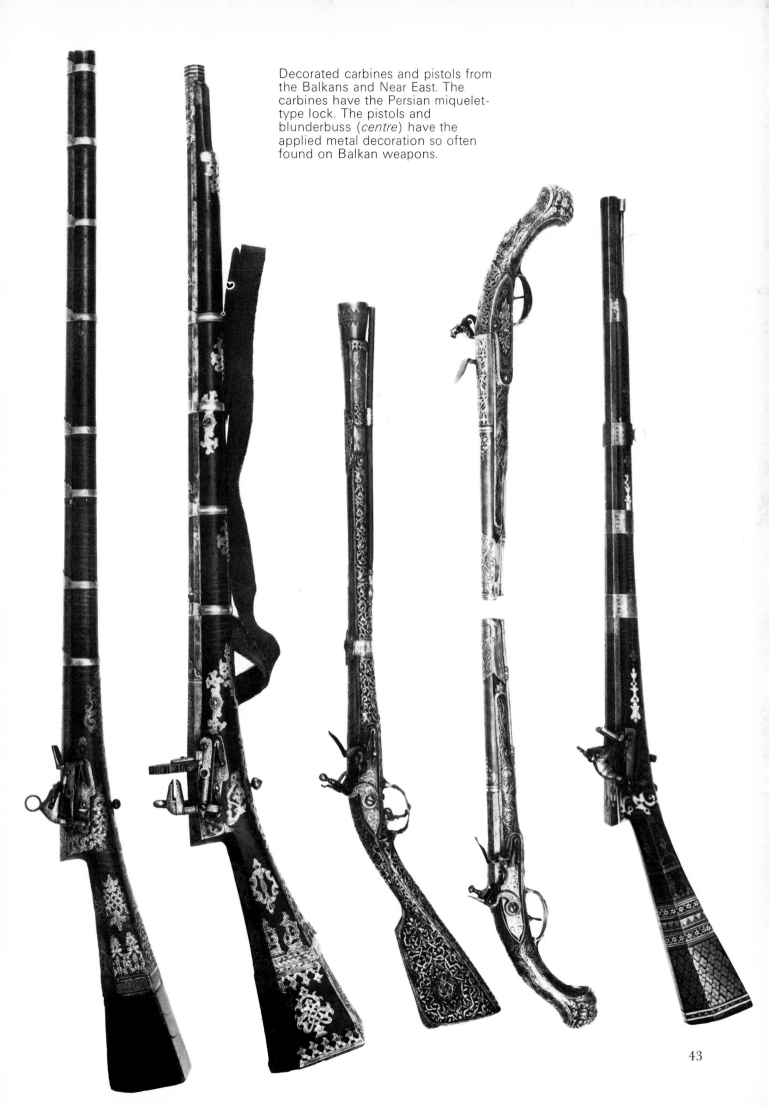

Decorated carbines and pistols from
the Balkans and Near East. The
carbines have the Persian miquelet-
type lock. The pistols and
blunderbuss (*centre*) have the
applied metal decoration so often
found on Balkan weapons.

43

Top. Elaborate Spanish percussion shotgun with 'Madrid' stock, shown with its shot belt and dating from the mid-nineteenth century.
Bottom. High-quality English percussion shotgun made *c* 1835 and fitted with Somerville's patent trigger-guard safety, which bolted the triggers forward until it was released by the left hand.
This called for a method of holding the gun that kept the left hand clear of the barrels should they burst — as many cheap ones did in those days.

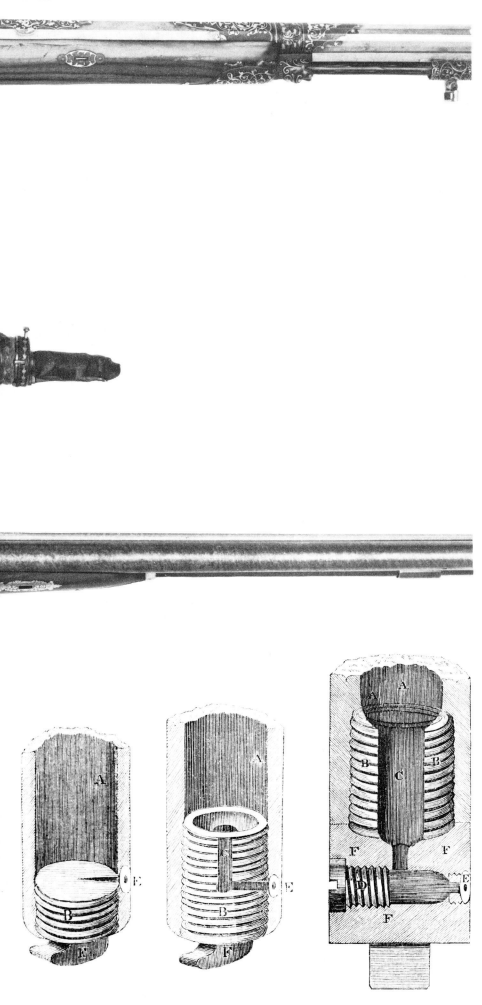

patent breech, introduced between 1780 and 1790. The usual flintlock breech consisted of a flat- or concave-faced breech plug screwed into the barrel. The flame from the pan went through the barrel wall to in front of the breech plug and lit the main powder charge. This design had two faults. The flame took a little time to pass from the pan to the main charge along the vent, and when it did reach the main charge it merely lit it, so that the charge was ignited fairly slowly.

The patent breech was constructed with an ante-chamber in the breech just inside a thin vent plug. This ante-chamber was connected to the main breech chamber by a small hole about $\frac{1}{8}$ in (3.2 mm) wide in such a way that a small part of the powder charge entered the main chamber on loading. When the gun was fired, the flame went quickly through the short vent to the ante-chamber and lit the powder in it, which then blasted a jet of flame into the main charge through the small hole. By this means the time from pulling the trigger to the actual discharge was reduced and, more importantly, the powder was burnt more quickly, enabling the barrel length to be reduced to about 30 in (76 cm) from the 36 in (91 cm) or more formerly needed.

This shorter barrel length, coupled with the use of lightweight twist barrels, enabled the makers to produce a double-barrelled gun of reasonable weight, and these became common from about 1800 onwards, usually in fairly small bores of 16 to 20. The double 12-bore did not become common until the 1840s.

Far left and centre
Forms of breeching used before the invention of the patent breech, and which remained in use for cheaper weapons until the end of the flintlock period: the common plug (*far left*) and the chamber plug (*centre*).

Left
The great invention: Nock's patent breech of 1787.

Rifles in the eighteenth century developed along three separate paths. In Britain the breech-loader was the most common type, although any rifle was a rarity until about 1780. Interest in rifles was then aroused by their use in the American War of Independence (1775–83), and British rifles, often with imported German barrels, began to appear. Most of these rifles were muzzle-loaders of under 16 bore, with fairly extreme rifling twists of a half to three-quarter turn in a 30-in (76-cm) barrel. The need to import German barrels dwindled once British makers had mastered the art of rifling, and German barrels are rare by 1800.

Further publicity for rifles came with the formation of the Corps of Riflemen in 1800, and of Volunteer rifle units to resist Napoleon's expected invasion. Starved of action, the Volunteers spent their time in target practice and inter-unit competitions, often reported in the public press. Knowledge of, and interest in, rifle shooting grew rapidly.

At first the influence of the military rifle on the sporting rifle was beneficial, as Baker, the designer of the Army rifle, had, with great good sense, chosen a rifling twist of only a quarter turn in a 30-in (76-cm) barrel. This enabled it to be loaded easily with a patched ball pressed in by the thumb, and to burn the large charge of about one-third of the bullet's weight of powder without stripping. This gave a high velocity and a low trajectory, so that errors in range estimation were of less account. Some sporting rifles were made with Baker's pattern of rifling and were excellent weapons.

Unfortunately, the enthusiastic target shots of the period found that a more rapid twist gave more accuracy. A book entitled *Scloppetaria*, published in 1808, made the point very strongly. But the accuracy was hard bought. The powder charge had to be reduced to stop the bullets from stripping, thus making the trajectory more curved. Also, to make them grip the rifling better, larger balls were used which had to be hammered into the muzzle, or forced in by ingenious levers. Not least, the more twisted rifling and the tighter bullets made it difficult to load with more than a few shots' powder fouling in the barrel.

On the other hand, for the target shooter who knew the range to a yard, had no need for velocity or penetration, and had ample time to load and swab out the barrel, the system seemed excellent. The gunsmiths, who seem to have been rather out of touch with actual requirements, made sporting rifles with similarly extreme rifling twists, these being soon fitted with the improved percussion lock which became common in the 1820s.

As it happened, the period 1820 to 1900 saw extensive use of sporting rifles as India, and later Africa, were flooded with expatriates eager to shoot the apparently inexhaustible numbers of big game. At home, rifles of the rook and rabbit type, weapons of light weight and small bore, were popular. The small-bore weapons worked well with the rapid rifling twists and percussion locks, as the

46

Right
Light 40-bore rook and rabbit rifle
of 1827 by the leading maker J.
Purdey. This is an early example of
a very common form of nineteenth-
century rifle.

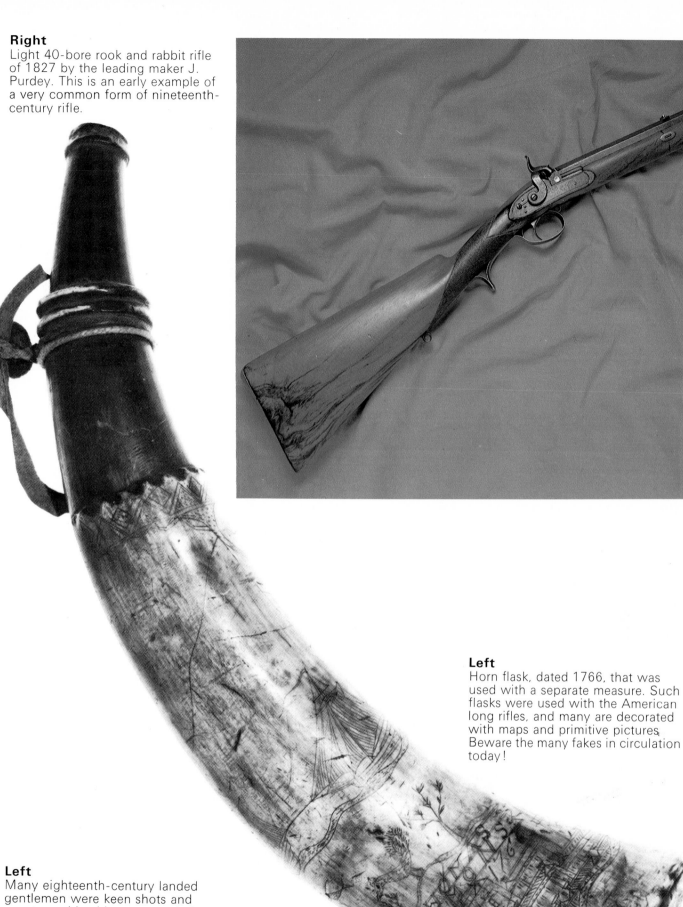

Left
Horn flask, dated 1766, that was
used with a separate measure. Such
flasks were used with the American
long rifles, and many are decorated
with maps and primitive pictures.
Beware the many fakes in circulation
today!

Left
Many eighteenth-century landed
gentlemen were keen shots and
spent considerable sums on their
guns. This portrait, *circa* 1750, by
the famous English artist Thomas
Gainsborough, shows Mr Andrews
carrying his long fowling piece.
National Gallery, London.

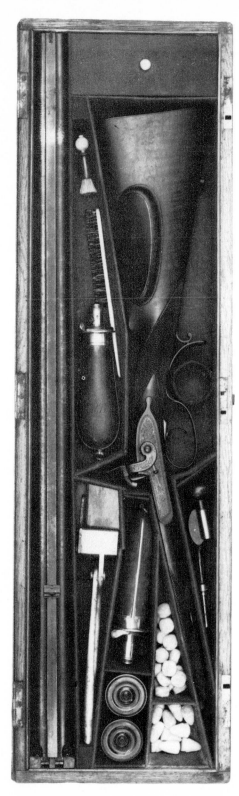

Double-barrelled percussion rifle by William Moore & Co. of London, No. 1641. The Damascus barrels are fitted with leaf sights. A baize-lined oak case contains the gun, powder flasks, mould, and various tools.

small balls, usually under 40 bore, were not so liable to strip. But with larger-bore big-game rifles the results were disastrous. The powerful flame of the percussion cap lit the powder too quickly, increasing even more the likelihood of the ball's stripping at the moment of initial acceleration. All the gunsmiths could think of to ensure accuracy was to reduce the powder charge still further. It did not occur to them to use larger-grained, slower-burning powder, or to reduce the pitch of the rifling. The powder charges became quite ridiculously small. Contemporary sources record $1\frac{1}{2}$ drachms (2.66 grams) for a 16-bore, and $1\frac{3}{4}$ drachms (3.1 grams) for a 13-bore, compared with the 4 drachms (7.09 grams) of the 20-bore Baker rifle. Even William Moore, the leading rifle maker of the time, could manage no more than $2\frac{1}{2}$ drachms (4.43 grams) in a 16-bore.

For sporting purposes such rifles were, to quote the late owner of the 13-bore above, 'quite useless and absurd', as the curved trajectory made hitting at an unknown range a matter of very accurate range estimation or pure luck, and even if it hit, the bullet lacked penetration and shocking power. So low was the opinion of rifles held by contemporary shots that they were seldom used for big-game shooting. Sir Samuel White Baker, an expert shot, reported in 1845 that there were no rifles in Ceylon. Big-game shooting was done with 16- or 14-bore shotguns, using a spherical ball and a double charge of powder.

As far as the spherical-ball rifle was concerned, the state of the art remained in the doldrums until 1863 when Lieutenant Forsyth, stationed in India, produced his book *The Sporting Rifle* and suggested the remedy. He pointed out that most sporting shots were at ranges of under 150 yd (137 m), so that long-range accuracy was unimportant. He therefore reduced the pitch of his rifling to a turn in 8 ft 8 in (2.64 m) for a 14-bore. This enabled it to burn large charges of powder without stripping while remaining easy to load. It seems so obvious now, it is surprising that no-one thought of it earlier.

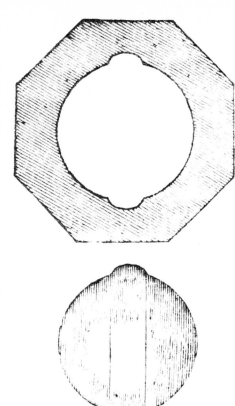

To eliminate the problem of the bullet's stripping, new forms of rifling were invented in which the bullets were cast with projections which fitted into the rifling grooves. The first of these was invented, or perhaps re-discovered, in 1836. This was the two-groove. The ball was cast with a belt round it, raised about $\frac{1}{16}$ in (1.6 mm) from the surface. The barrel had two deep grooves diametrically opposed to each other into which the belt fitted mechanically. A greased patch was used for lubrication. It is difficult to know whether the system was a success or not. The Army enthusiastically adopted it, and later equally vehemently damned it. But a great many sporting rifles were made as two-grooves, so it must have had some virtues. The idea was developed further by General Jacob in India, who around 1850 evolved a four-grooved rifle firing a cylindro-conical bullet, and by Purdey, who produced a very successful two-groove rifle firing conical bullets of 40 bore which was extensively used for deer stalking in the late '50s and early '60s, when the spherical-ball two-groove was obsolescent. To emphasize their high velocity, Purdey called his weapons 'Express' rifles.

Left
Two-groove rifling and bullet,
c 1840.

Below
From top to bottom.
A 4-bore rifle by J. Burrow of
Preston, c 1855, an unusually heavy
weapon even for its period. The
ramrod is made of brass for extra
strength.
A single-barrelled Whitworth
sporting rifle of c 1865 — very
accurate but with a high trajectory
at sporting ranges and little shocking
power.
Seven-barrelled goose rifle by
Forsyth & Co, c 1827. All the barrels
went off together, the hope being
that at least one bullet would hit
the goose!

Students of military and target rifles of the period 1850 to 1865 may wonder if the hollow-based Minié and the Whitworth and other 'small-bore' .45 in (11.4 mm) cylindro-conical bullets were used for sporting purposes. They were, but in very small numbers since they were almost useless. There were several reasons for this. The conical-nosed, solid bullets tended to penetrate too easily, without giving the shock to the animal's system which was required. No reliable expanding-nosed bullet was invented until the mid-1860s. But a greater disadvantage lay in the relationship between velocity, recoil and rifle weight. A rifle heavier than 9 lb (4 kg) was difficult to carry in the heat of India, where most British big-game shooting took place. Elongated bullets obviously weighed more than spherical balls of the same bore. So for the same muzzle velocity a cylindro-conical ball would kick more than a spherical ball of the same bore in the same weight of rifle. Or, more to the point, if both were loaded to give the same, just bearable, kick, the cylindro-conical bullet would have to have lower velocity, and hence a more curved trajectory

at sporting ranges. While the patched-ball rifle was limited by an extreme rifling twist, the cylindro-conical bullet might have a higher velocity, but once Forsyth's gradual twist came into use it was definitely inferior. Any effort to lessen the recoil of the cylindro-conical bullet by reducing its diameter merely reduced the size of the hole in the animal.

Efforts to increase the bullet's shock effect were made by various inventors. Spherical balls were cast with clay cores which were then picked out and replaced with detonating powder, but they were tiresome to manufacture and little used. General Jacob produced a cylindro-conical bullet with a tubular hole in the nose into which was pressed a copper tube containing detonating composition and gunpowder. This exploded on impact to open out the nose of the bullet. It seems to have been somewhat uncertain in its action, as well as being extremely dangerous to carry. The ramrod had a recessed head designed to permit safe loading.

Lieutenant Forsyth invented an expanding bullet in two parts, swaged together with a rather insensitive

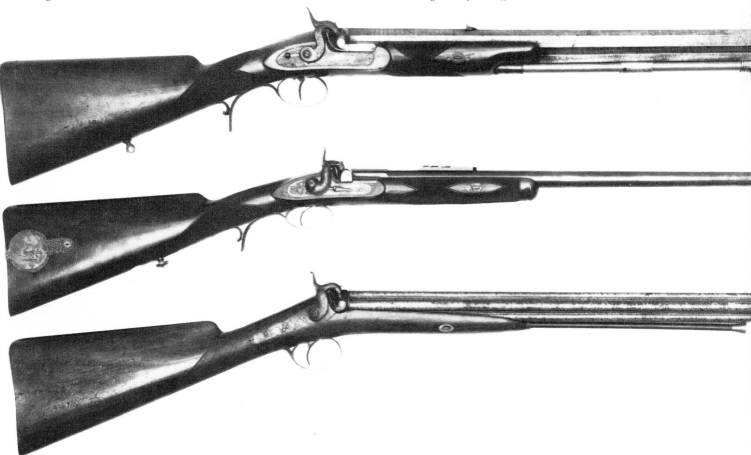

Below
A quartet of flasks.
From left to right.
Shot flask with see-saw cut-off by Hawksley, *c* 1860.
Rifle-shooting powder flask with a lever-operated cut-off to reduce the charge variations, *c* 1865.
Conventional flask with a telescopic nozzle for different charges.
Elaborate flask of horn and German silver, complete with its original carrying cords.

Bottom
Single-barrelled 10-bore rifle, made by A. Henry of Edinburgh in about 1872. It is a typical big-game rifle of the period with the double-grip action.

Right
Percussion sporting guns with browned barrels, both made by Westley Richards, a famous Birmingham gunmaker. The flasks held powder or shot and were available in a great variety of patterns and sizes.

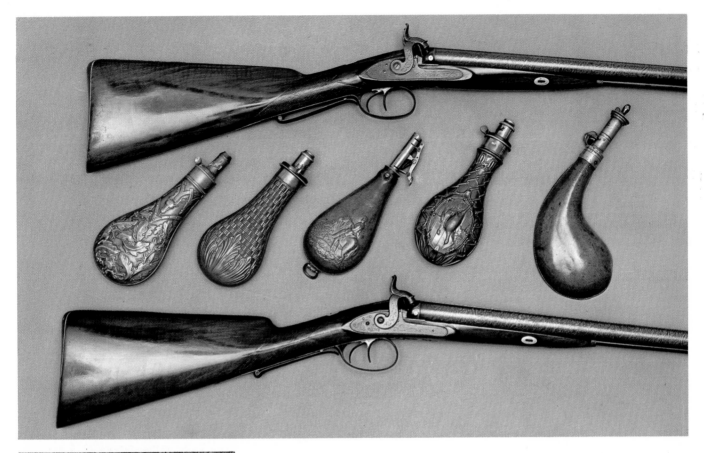

Above
Hunting knife with horn grip made in India *c* 1865 by Boput of Nagpore.

detonating mixture held in a chamber inside. This seems to have worked better, or so he assures us in his book, because the bullet had to be considerably deformed before it exploded, giving more time for penetration. In fact, as he noted himself, the bullet also worked quite well as an expanding bullet without the detonating powder. This was because it simply mushroomed.

Breech-loading was adopted generally for British sporting rifles in the period 1860–70, a little later than for shotguns. There were in fact several reasons for this delay. The early breech-loaders were more expensive than muzzle-loaders since they were more complicated, and sportsmen were, and still are, very conservative. On an entirely mechanical level, the early breech-loading actions were not very strong, especially the double-barrelled ones, and most big-game rifles were double-barrelled. It took a few years to develop actions capable of taking the much higher breech pressures of rifles. The early rifle cartridges were not too strong either, being made of rolled brass sheet with a riveted-on iron base, or of cardboard with a brass base like a

modern shotgun case. It was one thing to use an early breech-loading shotgun against grouse in England with no risk to life or limb and gunsmiths in every town. It was quite another to trust one's life to an early breech-loading rifle in the Indian jungle, perhaps hundreds of miles from civilization.

However, as in all things, improvements were quickly made. The Patent Office was deluged between 1865 and 1880 with inventions for better and stronger breech actions. Then, around 1870, the solid-drawn, one-piece brass cartridge case appeared. Although the rolled brass case was used for years afterwards, the solid-drawn case was a milestone. It could take higher pressures and hence give higher velocities. It was far more resistant to damp than the rolled case, an important point in conditions of high humidity, where wet powder could mean death from a charging animal. Once fired, the case could be extracted easily with little risk of jamming in the chamber.

Not very surprisingly, the breech-loaders soon swept the muzzle-loaders from the field. Their rapidity of loading was an overwhelming advantage. Another, less obvious, was that they could be unloaded at the end of the day's shooting if unfired. Muzzle-loading rifles were extremely difficult to unload as the bullet fitted so tightly. The usual practice in the jungle had been to fire off the loaded rifles in the evening, and to clean them ready for use the next day – a tedious task, but one that had to be done, since few would rely on a muzzle-loader which had been unfired for several days.

The period 1875–1900 was perhaps the peak of the career of the British sporting rifle. It was 'the thing' to go hunting in India and Africa, and the gunsmiths produced splendid and functional weapons in large numbers. Fearsome batteries are recorded. One writer, F.J. Jackson, had the following armoury in 1894:

A single 4-bore rifle weighing 21 lb (9.5 kg), sighted for 50, 100, and 150 yd (45, 91 and 137 m), shooting 12 drachms (21.26 grams) of powder and a spherical bullet

A double 8-bore rifle, weighing 15 lb (6.8 kg), sighted for 100 and 200 yd (91 and 201 m), shooting 12 drachms (21.26 grams) of powder and a spherical bullet

A double .500 (12.7-mm) Express, sighted for 100 and 200 yd (91 and 183 m), bored for long bottle-shaped cases, with a 'Magnum' case shooting 6 drachms (10.63 grams) of powder and long bullets of three kinds – solid, small-hole, and copper-tube

A 12-bore shotgun

A single .450 (11.43-mm) Express with telescopic sight up to 300 yards (274 m) for long shots when game was wild

A .44 (11.2-mm) Winchester carbine, a wonderfully accurate and first-rate little weapon for Gazella Thomsoni and such small game

A .295 (7.5-mm) rook rifle

A 12-bore Paradox by Messrs Holland

The heavier rifles were carried by a gun bearer most of the time, which is why Lieutenant Forsyth was against them for normal use, claiming that they were never to hand when urgently needed.

'Magnum' cases held more powder than the standard ones, which held 5 drachms (8.86 grams) in a .5 in (12.7 mm) Express. The small-hole and copper-tube bullets were variations of the Express bullet of the time, which had a hole down the middle nearly to the base to lighten it and so permit high velocities without excessive recoil. The hole also assisted the expansion on impact. Solid bullets kicked viciously, and were used only for great penetration.

The single .450 (11.43-mm) Express was used for long-range shooting because double rifles were never as accurate as singles, owing to the great difficulty of fixing the two barrels together so that their bullets hit the same spot. The telescopic sight had been in use for some years, with examples dating from about 1840, but had only recently been made sufficiently shock-proof to be used in the field. The Paradox weapon was a shotgun also capable of firing light bullets with reasonable accuracy to about 100 yd (91 m).

Quite soon, by the 1880s, the supply of game began to run low, and the heyday of the English sporting rifle was over. The double rifle con-

Above and left
Buffalo shooting with single-shot Sharps rifles. The forked sticks were used as rifle rests for long-range accuracy.

tinues to be used to the present day for big-game shooting, but the single-shot rifles have all been superseded by the magazine weapons described later in the book.

On the Continent the development was more gradual. The wheel-lock was still used in Germany until the eighteenth century, probably because of its reliability. Continental rifles tend to be less well finished than English ones, as might be expected since they were used by far more levels of society. The large bores used by the British were not so popular, but fairly extreme rifling twists were. They seem to have been fired with small powder charges and this, with a very tight bullet and patch, sometimes tapped into the barrel with a mallet, seems to have overcome the stripping problem. In the eighteenth century and later, all game, like grouse today, was driven towards a line of guns, so perhaps a flat trajectory was not as important as accuracy at short range. Almost all German and Swiss rifles have hair triggers, unlike most British rifles. Pin- and needle-fire rifles are quite common.

But North America was the place where the sporting rifle was most used. The early settlers may have brought rifles with them, but they were certainly common from about 1720 onwards. The early rifles, like their European contemporaries, were from 16 to 20-bore and fairly short in the barrel. The main targets were deer and small game, and so while there was no need for heavy balls, a flat trajectory and accuracy were essential. The makers quickly adapted their weapons to the demand, and by about 1740 American flintlock rifles were of quite small bore. Colonel Hanger, a British officer who fought in the War of Independence, says of them, 'the barrels weigh about 6 lbs. 2 or 3 oz and carry a ball no larger than 36 to the pound; at least I never saw one of larger calibre and I have seen many hundreds and hundreds'. The heavy barrels would have helped accuracy and the small bore would have permitted large powder charges without stripping; the latter point is borne out by the fact that American rifles were fired with half the bullet's weight of powder, giving a charge of over three drachms (5.32 grams) in a 40-bore. The barrel lengths went up to 40–45 in (1.0–1.1 m), possibly to give time for the burning of the large charges of what was probably rather poor, slow-burning gunpowder.

Such rifles must have had muzzle velocities of well over 2,000 fps (610 mps), although the light bullets would have lost velocity fairly quickly. They were at their best up to about 150 yd (137 m). An indication of the flatness of the trajectory is given by the fact that American long rifles hardly ever have adjustable sights.

Few American rifles are 'fine' arms. The emphasis was on cheapness and utility, although many are graceful, with elaborately decorated patch boxes in the butts. The crescent butt plate was almost universal. Eighteenth-century examples are usually fully stocked to the muzzle, but later rifles are often half-stocked with a rib under the barrel to carry the ramrod pipes. Many nineteenth-century American sporting rifles were rifled to shoot 'picket' bullets, cylindro-conical projectiles which gave great accuracy. Indeed, the difference between the target and sporting arms of the period is often very slight.

Breech-loading started in the United States with the use of capping breech-loaders, notably the Sharps. In such weapons, of which there were many types, the paper cartridge, which burnt away, was ignited by an external cap. Their use never became general, and they were soon superseded by metallic cartridge weapons.

Repeating rifles (see Chapter 5) were in general use in America almost as soon as breech-loading metallic cartridges became available. Single-shot rifles continued for a while, for at first they alone could take the high pressures of the powerful cartridges used for buffalo hunting. The buffalo, hunted almost to extinction to feed the railroad-construction workers, had become understandably shy of mankind, and had to be shot at long range with what were akin to sporting target rifles. But soon the repeaters took over.

The introduction of the percussion lock was wholly beneficial as far as the shotgun was concerned. Development continued along similar lines all over the world. At last the charge

Above
Top. Double-barrelled, 12-bore shotgun elaborately decorated with engraving and chiselling.
Bottom. A 12-bore, double-barrelled gun by Stephen Grant of London. It has a side-mounted spring bayonet which is most unusual on a weapon of this date. Both guns were made in the late nineteenth century.

Above
The weapon that launched the modern shotgun: a Lefaucheux pin-fire of the 1850s.

Right
A pin-fire shotgun and cartridges. This is a late example, *c* 1860, by the Edinburgh gunsmith J. Dickson and has the powerful double-grip breech action widely used in double rifles.

was fired quickly and reliably as soon as the trigger was pulled, faster even than the patent-breeched flintlock. The patent breech was no longer necessary, and the considerable skill required to make a good flintlock ceased to be important. Enormous numbers of double- and single-barrelled shotguns were made in the period 1825–65 – not all of them, it must be said, of very good quality, for Birmingham and Liège, the centres of gun manufacture, turned out large numbers of second-rate weapons for export. A great many, rather surprisingly, went to America, whose extensive arms industry the Europeans could undercut by using their cheap hand labour.

Efforts were made to develop some means of holding the shot charge together for longer distances. The most successful seems to have been the Eley Cartridge. This was a form of shrapnel. In one type the shot charge was enclosed in a wire bag inside a thin paper outer case fixed to a wad. Theoretically, the paper ruptured and burnt away on dis-charge and the shot then escaped from the wire. Justifiable doubts were expressed as to whether the shot always escaped, for if it did not, a solid and lethal projectile was left. A later version replaced the wire cage with a packing of bone dust in the paper cover. This type was widely used.

Real progress was made in the 1870s. Guns bored with very slight increases in barrel diameter towards the breech and the muzzle had been found to shoot better than guns bored with the same diameter from end to end, but the gain was small. Fierce argument took place at the time over who invented 'choke boring', as it was termed, but the great exponent and maker of choke-bored guns was W W Greener. The form he used, still universal today, consisted of coning the barrel from about 3 in (76.2 mm) to about $\frac{1}{2}$ in (12.7 mm) from the muzzle. The reduction in diameter is .005–.04 in (.127–1.01 mm) in a 12-bore, depending on the amount of concentration required of the shot charge. The acceptance of choke boring was encouraged by elaborate trials of the different makes which were widely reported in the sporting press.

A breech-loading shotgun was exhibited in London at the Great Exhibition of 1851 by the great French gunsmith Lefaucheux. It was a pin-fire taking a cartridge rather like a modern shotgun case with a brass base. The paper case expanded very slightly and sealed the breech, solving the problem that had dogged all previous designs. Little gas leaked past the pin itself, as it was carried in a paper plug, pressed into the base of the cartridge, which closed around it as the pressure rose. Early pin-fire cartridges had no rims, and were extracted by gripping the pins, but rims were soon added.

Despite enthusiastic promotion by the British gunsmith Lang, the pin-fire did not sell well at first. The action of Lefaucheux's double-barrelled break-open shotgun, similar to one of the present day, was not very strong and tended to work loose after a few hundred shots. The cartridges were more expensive than the shot and powder of a muzzle-loader. But development proceeded. *The Field*, a sporting paper, was swamped with contradictory letters from satisfied

Late nineteenth-century double-barrelled sporting guns
From top to bottom
A 6-bore breech-loading rifle with 24-inch barrels. Marked at the breech R. B. Rodda & Co. Gunmakers by Appointment to H.E. The Viceroy of India, H.R.H. The Duke of Edinburgh, London and 7 and 8 Dalhousie Square, Calcutta.
Pin-fire, 16-bore gun with 29-inch barrels inscribed 'Damas Laminette', *circa* 1860.
Needle-fire shotgun with 12-bore, 32¼-inch barrels made by Sauer & Sohn a Suhl, *circa* 1860.

and dissatisfied owners of breech-loaders, and organized trials in 1858 to determine if they were better than muzzle-loaders. These trials were inconclusive, but in a later one held in 1862 the breech-loaders won 5 to 1, and their general adoption followed very quickly. The pin-fire cartridge did not last very long in England, but it can still be bought in France. It was thought dangerous to carry and was difficult to load with cold hands.

Charles Lancaster, a leading mak-er of the time, produced in 1852 an effective centre-fire cartridge with the detonating compound sandwich-ed between its base and a perforated copper disc inside the case. His guns, however, were extremely expensive.

Joseph Needham produced a needle-fire shotgun in which a thin pin penetrated the base wads of a paper cartridge; this burnt away on discharge, leaving the wads to be pushed forward and fired out by the next cartridge. It seems to have been

reasonably successful, but the wads must have ruined the shot pattern, it being a fact of shotgun ballistics that the over-shot wad should be as thin as possible to prevent its deflecting the charge.

The cartridge case used today was introduced to Britain by G H Daw in 1861, but was really a development of earlier designs by the Frenchmen C Pottet and G E Schneider. Daw's application for a patent was not upheld, and his cartridge was

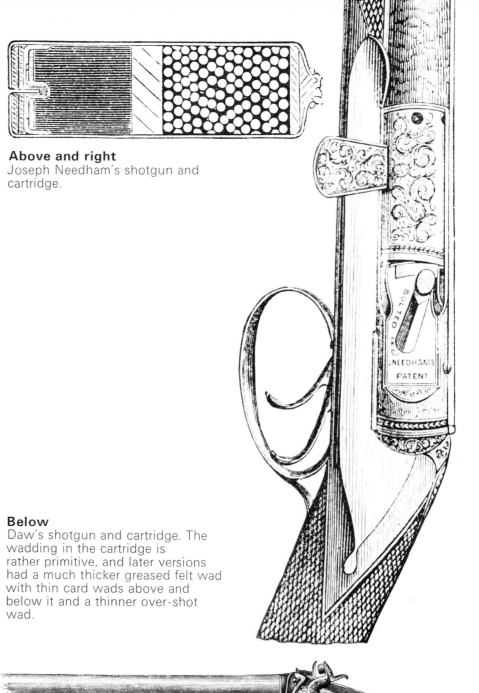

Above and right
Joseph Needham's shotgun and cartridge.

Below
Daw's shotgun and cartridge. The wadding in the cartridge is rather primitive, and later versions had a much thicker greased felt wad with thin card wads above and below it and a thinner over-shot wad.

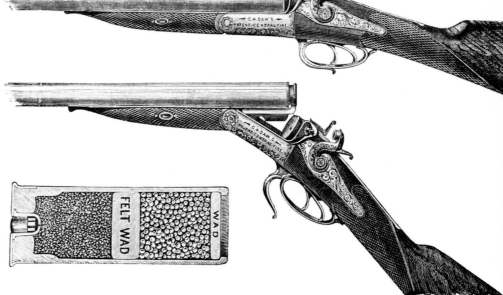

FELT WAD

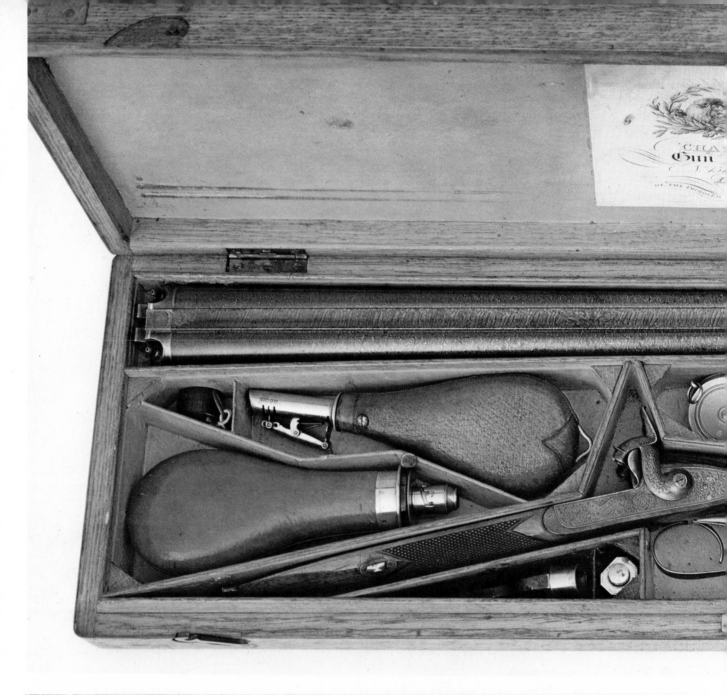

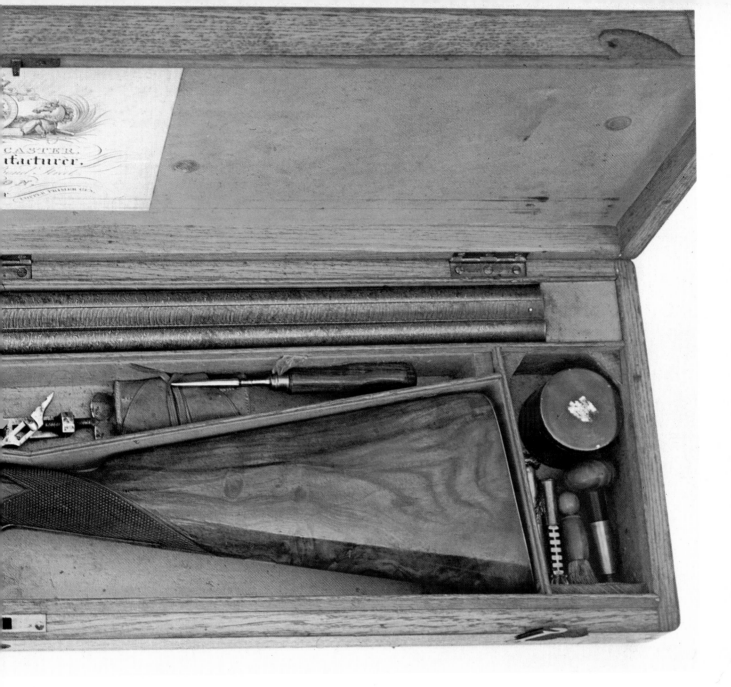

Left
A double-barrelled 8-bore wildfowling gun by J. Dougall of London, c 1872. The Dougall action was very strong, and was much used between 1860 and 1875 despite being awkward to operate.

Above
Most sporting guns of the nineteenth century were made to fit into a case, as does this example by Charles Lancaster of London. The accessories of the double-barrelled, 14-bore percussion gun are carried in the various special compartments. W. Keith Neal, Guernsey.

universally adopted by gunmakers.

Numerous actions were invented in the period 1860–80. The British stuck to the side-by-side double-barrelled shotgun, but the improvements made to this type alone would fill a book. They were devoted mainly to strengthening the breech fastening, eliminating the external hammers, easing the cocking on a hammerless gun, improving the safety, and making the same trigger fire both barrels in succession, (a very difficult mechanism to design, since the recoil makes the shooter press the trigger a second time involuntarily). On the Continent the over-and-under barrel arrangement is also widely used. The Germans developed a weapon in which two shotgun

barrels were combined with a rifle barrel – making a weapon suitable for any likely game.

The Americans made double shotguns for a short time, but adopted repeating single-barrel guns as soon as they became available. One reason for this may have been that the Americans were less conservative than the Europeans, but a more likely explanation is that the skilled work necessary to make a good double shotgun was very expensive in America, and machine-made repeaters were cheaper.

Two more important improvements were still to be made: steel barrels and smokeless powder. Forge-welding can only be carried out with very low-carbon steel or iron, which is

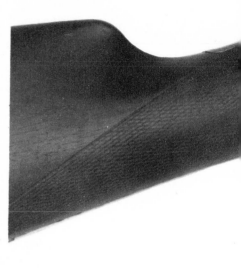

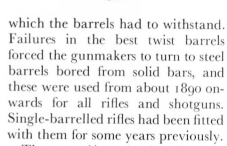

A heavy bag for a game-shooting party in the 1880s: the splendid desolation which surrounds the Prince of Wales could only be an artist's representation.

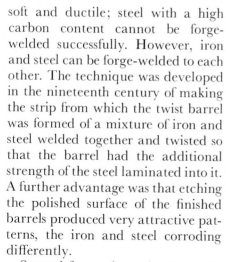

soft and ductile; steel with a high carbon content cannot be forge-welded successfully. However, iron and steel can be forge-welded to each other. The technique was developed in the nineteenth century of making the strip from which the twist barrel was formed of a mixture of iron and steel welded together and twisted so that the barrel had the additional strength of the steel laminated into it. A further advantage was that etching the polished surface of the finished barrels produced very attractive patterns, the iron and steel corroding differently.

Several factors brought about the end of the twist barrel. To weld a complete twist barrel without any faults in the welds was extremely difficult, especially one made of laminated steel and iron. As described earlier, it was the custom to ream out the bore until no faults were visible. Cartridges, however, dictated a standard bore diameter, and more barrels had to be rejected after a great deal of expensive work had been put into them. Also, breech-loading enabled the owner to look down his barrels and detect where minute faults in the original surface had become larger through corrosion. But lack of strength was the decider. Choke-boring and smokeless powder increased the stresses which the barrels had to withstand. Failures in the best twist barrels forced the gunmakers to turn to steel barrels bored from solid bars, and these were used from about 1890 onwards for all rifles and shotguns. Single-barrelled rifles had been fitted with them for some years previously.

The general introduction of smokeless powder was delayed by the extremely variable strength of the early makes. Nor was it appreciated initially that the power of the cap and the exact compression of the powder charge were far more critical for consistent performance than with gunpowder. Not only were the shot patterns of all the early smokeless

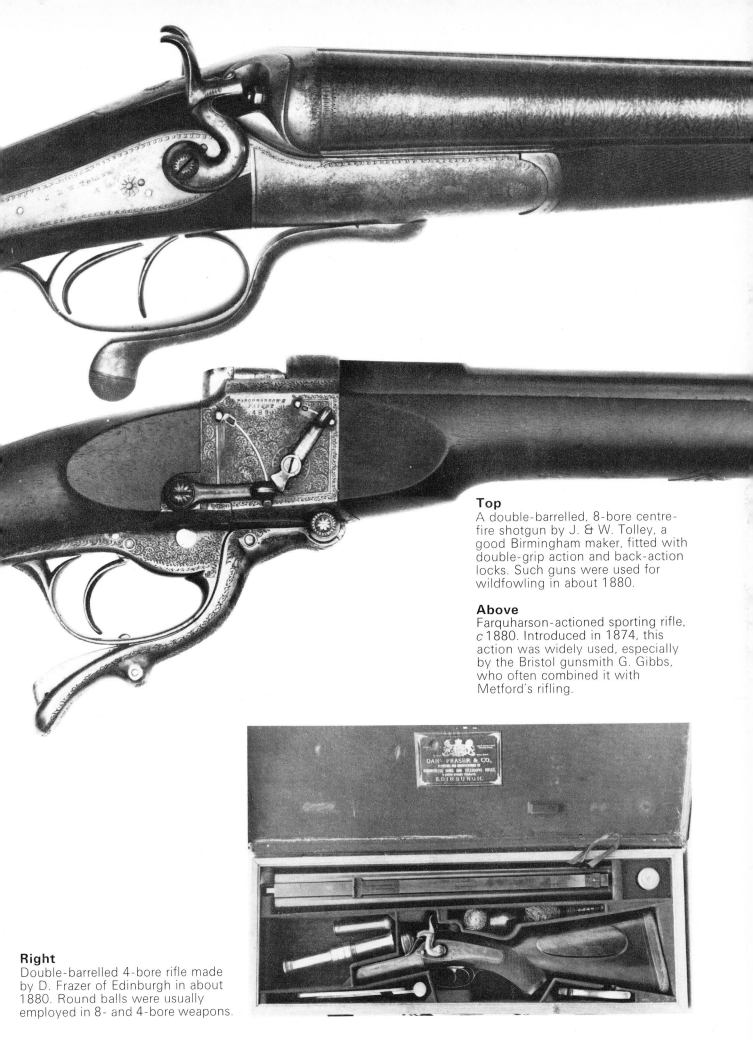

Top
A double-barrelled, 8-bore centre-fire shotgun by J. & W. Tolley, a good Birmingham maker, fitted with double-grip action and back-action locks. Such guns were used for wildfowling in about 1880.

Above
Farquharson-actioned sporting rifle, c 1880. Introduced in 1874, this action was widely used, especially by the Bristol gunsmith G. Gibbs, who often combined it with Metford's rifling.

Right
Double-barrelled 4-bore rifle made by D. Frazer of Edinburgh in about 1880. Round balls were usually employed in 8- and 4-bore weapons.

cartridges very unpredictable, guns even blew up. The problem was especially acute with double-barrelled big-game rifles, as the powder charges were large and the safety margins small.

However, the advantages of smokeless powder – little fouling and a clear view of the target after firing – encouraged research, and smokeless shotgun cartridges were common, though by no means universal, by around 1890. For big-game rifles the change was delayed for the larger calibres until the twentieth century.

Selection of accessories.
Top row, from left to right.
A T-shaped nipple key with screwed-in pricker to clear the nipple, and screw-capped arms to hold spare nipples.
Nipple key with screwed-in pricker.
Cutter for making wads. This example cuts wads with minute indentations in their edges to release the air when ramming.
Austrian cap dispenser. Spring jaws at the end of the neck release the cap when it is placed on the nipple, and a spring-loaded plunger feeds the caps to the jaws.
Bottom row, left to right.
Flintlock tool combining two sizes of screwdriver with a brass pin to clear the vent. The two parts press into each other.
Device to prick powder down the nipple in case of misfires.
English cap dispenser showing the method of feeding the caps.

Target Shooting

Richard Whittaker

Target shooting and target rifles developed at different times and in different ways in Europe, in Great Britain, and in America. In Europe, target shooting seems to have started almost as soon as small arms were adopted: a shooting match at 200 metres, for example, was advertised at Eichstädt in 1477. The sixteenth century saw tremendous enthusiasm for the sport and almost every town had its shooting association, which was a centre of social and sporting activity. Their sets of rules, of which many survive, were most elaborate, and sensible too, with strict safety regulations. Several illustrations of sixteenth-century shooting ranges also exist, revealing scenes of extra-ordinary modernity. The range for a shooting tournament at Zurich in 1504, for instance, had targets with circular rings, markers in armoured boxes with indicators to show where the bullets hit the targets, covered firing points, and a score-keeper in an office. Only the weapons and clothes seem antique. Pictorial targets were often used, sometimes with racial or political overtones, such as paintings of Turkish horsemen, the Turks being the arch enemies of Europe in the sixteenth and seventeenth centuries.

The Thirty Years' War (1618–48) upset the settled way of life in which the shooting associations flourished, and they became less common until the nineteenth century. Their decline in the seventeenth century may also have been due to the general revulsion against war and all its crafts that the Thirty Years' War engendered. It has been suggested, too, that civilian rifle shooting, especially among townspeople, was discouraged in the eighteenth century by absolute monarchs fearful of revolt.

The sport revived in the nineteenth century, but declined again when rapid developments in rifle design in the early breech-loading period made the possession of up-to-date weapons very costly. Another factor, common to all countries at the time, was the difficulty of finding space for firing ranges as populations

Left
Competitive shooting enjoyed great popularity in the late nineteenth century. This engraving illustrates a match between US and Irish teams in 1875.

began to increase quite considerably.

It is not always easy to tell whether some sixteenth-century weapons were intended for target or game shooting. Rifles must have been used as soon as they were invented, as their advantages for target shooting were so manifest, but the only specific records relate to prohibitions on their use. Almost all European target shooting was done from a standing position at fairly short ranges, seldom more than 200 m. This was very sensible, as this position and range were also suitable for sporting shooting in forests with thick undergrowth. At first, the rifles were the owners' hunting weapons or heavier versions of them with superior sights. Small powder charges were used, since velocity was unimportant, and almost every form of rifling was tried. As with hunting rifles, the locks evolved from matchlocks to wheellocks, then to flintlocks and on to percussion locks and then to cartridges, the method still used.

Sixteenth-century target rifles continued to be built on the lines of hunting rifles, but with longer barrels, more weight – up to 16 lb (7.25 kg) quite often – and simple aperture back sights, some being fitted in a short tube to eliminate reflections. The hair trigger was universal. It was really a separate lock which was cocked by pulling a second trigger and then released by a light touch on the hair trigger itself.

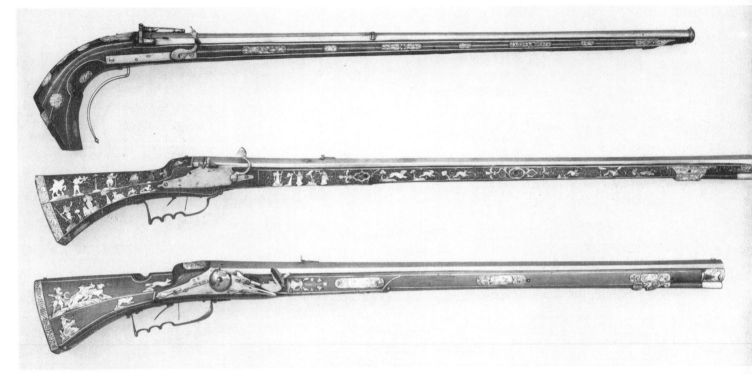

Above
Very early flintlock gun made for Louis XIII of France in about 1615 and numbered '134' in his *cabinet d'armes*.

Top
From top to bottom
A matchlock gun of *c* 1575 with a 'French' pattern stock.
Matchlock rifle with 'hair' or 'set' trigger, dating from the late sixteenth century.
Wheellock rifle of the early seventeenth century, also fitted with a 'set' trigger.
Tower of London Armouries.

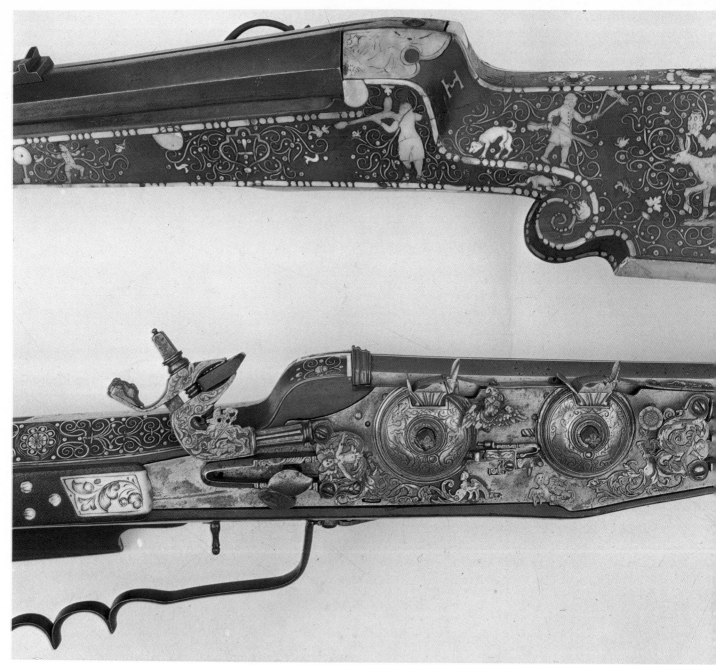

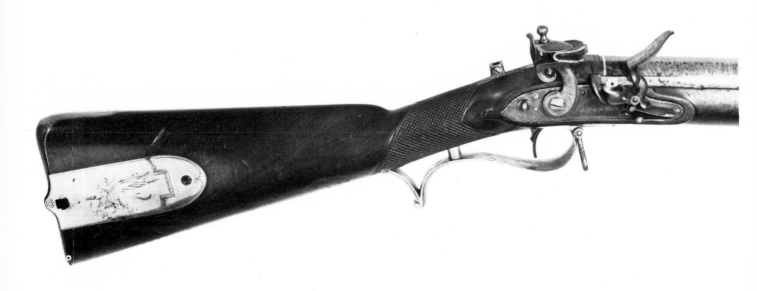

Below
Flintlock target rifle made by
Fenton *c* 1810 with a mounting for
an aperture back sight.

The custom of modelling target rifles on hunting rifles changed in the nineteenth century when a type of target rifle appeared in Germany and Switzerland that was specially designed for standing shooting. This weapon had a fairly short barrel of about 25–30 in (63–72 cm), a stock with a pronounced cheek rest, a hooked butt plate to stop it sliding up the shoulder, an adjustable palm rest in front of the trigger guard, which was itself continued down under the small of the stock with notches for the fingers of the right hand, and a complex aperture back sight. In this form of sight the shooter looked through a tiny hole instead of centring the fore sight in a 'V'. This type of rifle continued into the breech-loading period and was also used in America in the 1860s.

The exact date of the adoption of elongated bullets by Continental target shots is difficult to state with certainty, but it was probably around 1850, when the French Minié bullet became popular for military rifles. Long-range target rifles on the Brisish or American plan do not seem to have been developed at all in Europe until the advent of small-bore military rifles in the 1880s and 1890s. They were little different from the standard military rifles of the period.

There was virtually no target rifle shooting in England before 1800. As stated in the chapter on sporting rifles, the formation of the Corps of Riflemen in 1800 aroused interest in rifles, and between then and 1808, when the book *Scloppetaria* was published, the target shots discovered, as probably any Continental shot of the time could have told them, that a more extreme rifling twist gave more accuracy. The Baker rifle, for instance, could group its bullets into an 18 in (45 cm) circle at 100 yd (91 m) fairly consistently, whereas a William Moore rifle in *Scloppetaria* could group into 18 in (45 cm) at 200 yd (182 m) – a notable improvement, but with accompanying inconveniences only to be borne on the target range.

The sights described in *Scloppetaria* have been little improved to the present day. Even a telescopic sight with crosswires is described. Various

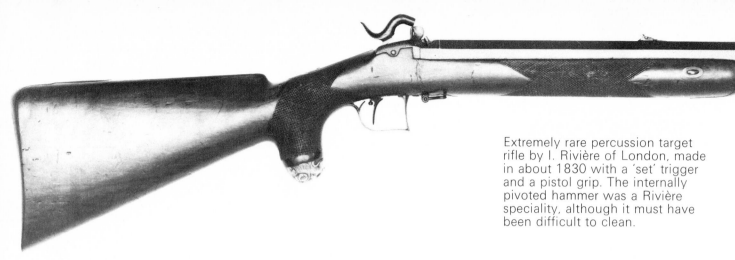

Extremely rare percussion target rifle by I. Rivière of London, made in about 1830 with a 'set' trigger and a pistol grip. The internally pivoted hammer was a Rivière speciality, although it must have been difficult to clean.

methods of firing rifles at long range were developed at the time, including the back position, in which the shooter lay on his back and fired the rifle between his feet, but the use of the top hat as a rifle rest might seem a little dated today.

Not much rifle shooting took place between 1815 and 1850. Once the threat of French invasion had passed, most of the Volunteer units disbanded and only a few rifle clubs kept up the sport. Then in 1851 came the adoption of the Minié rifle. In this weapon, developed in France by Captains Delvigne and Minié, the bullet, instead of being spherical, was a short cylinder with a conical nose and a hollow base. Of such a diameter that it could slide down the barrel easily, it made loading very simple, even if the barrel was dirty. When the powder ignited, the pressure expanded the base of the bullet into the rifling, so that the bullet sealed the barrel and, more important, gripped the rifling very effectively. To assist in the expansion, an iron cup was pressed into the hollow in the base of the bullet, though its usefulness was questionable. With the Minié bullet the age-old problem of stripping was solved.

Events followed swiftly. The Great Exhibition of 1851 encouraged interest in technology and arms. In 1853 Britain and France went to war with Russia. In 1859 it was thought that the French were again planning to invade Britain. Public and official interest in rifles revived.

Following extensive tests and the submission of rifles by leading gunmakers, an improved model of the Minié, known as the Enfield rifle, was adopted in 1853. It was a well-designed and serviceable weapon. However, the early models posed a severe problem: some were accurate and some were not, despite apparently being, as far as the Government Inspectors could determine, exactly the same. The Government called for advice on Sir Joseph Whitworth, a leading engineer of the age and a specialist in machine tools and precise measurement. He agreed to conduct experiments into the best form of rifling if the Government would pay the expenses, which it did, specifying only that he must use the same bullet weight and powder charge as the Government Enfield – a 530-grain bullet propelled by 70 grains of Government powder, which was not of very good quality at the time. Whitworth described it as the 'siftings of cannon powder'.

Whitworth revolutionized the accuracy of rifles in Britain. Before his time, rifle bullets had been short and fat, the Enfield bullet being .568 in (14.4 mm) in diameter before expansion and .875 in (22.2 mm) long. The Enfield rifle made a turn in 78 in (1.98 m) with three grooves. Whitworth's bullet was .45 in (11.43 mm) in diameter and 1.375 in (34.9 mm) long. His rifling made a turn in 20 in (50.8 cm) and was hexagonal in cross-section with rounded corners. The hexagonal form of bore he chose, was not, in fact, a very good one, as it collected the powder fouling too quickly, but he claimed that it was easy to cut accurately by machinery.

Whitworth first tried a cylindro-conical bullet with a hollow base to expand into the rifling, but could not obtain reliable expansion with the inferior Government powder. He then turned to a hardened bullet of hexagonal cross-section exactly fitting the bore, and only reverted to cylindrical bullets when he could use better gunpowder. The hexagonal bullet seems to have been the more accurate.

The improvement of accuracy and range was phenomenal: it was about three times more accurate than the Enfield. But the Whitworth rifle was not as suitable for service use. The powder fouling was a real problem and the high, for the time, barrel pressure eroded the nipples so quickly that they had to be bushed, or lined, with platinum. It was at its best as a target rifle and reigned supreme from 1860 to 1867.

The French invasion scare, like its predecessor, had stimulated the formation of Volunteer units, and these in turn begat the National Rifle Association in 1859. The NRA held its annual meetings on Wimbledon Common from 1860 to 1889 and thereafter at Bisley. For obvious reasons, the Volunteers used the .577 (14.6-mm) Enfield rifles with which they were armed, but special competitions were included for match rifles of any pattern. In addition, the second stage of the Queen's Prize was shot at 800, 900, and 1,000 yd (731, 823 and 914 m) with rifles selected at a trial earlier in the year. The Whitworth was the only suitable rifle at first, but competition was soon offered.

The Dublin gunsmith J Rigby and the Edinburgh gunsmith A Henry produced rifles which were, in effect, modified Whitworths. Both briefly used mechanically fitted bullets, but soon adopted cylindrical ones. The bullets were loaded from the muzzle with thin dry paper patches rolled

Right
The British Volunteer movement was the butt of many jokes by the humorous magazine *Punch*. Here Cook complains of the mess made made by the 'Master' as he cleans his Enfield rifle.

" *The 'orrid mess Master made my kitching in, and hisself too, a-cleaning that 'here dratted Rifle, after he'd been a booviackin' in the Park.*"

Below
Rifling becomes shallower and shallower, as demonstrated by these drawings of the successive Whitworth, Henry, Rigby and Metford systems.

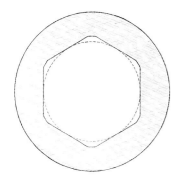 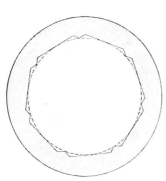 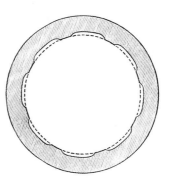 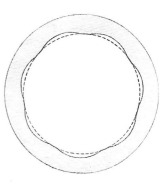

Right
Cased Whitworth military-type target rifle as used in the Queen's Prize competition contested on Wimbledon Common, London. Although accurate, it was subject to rapid powder fouling. The mould supplied in the case casts cylindrical bullets, although ready-made hexagonal bullets were generally used at that time, about 1865, for target shooting.

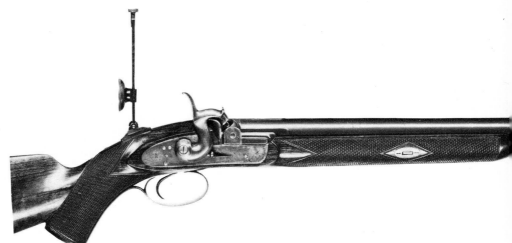

Right
Whitworth long-range target rifle, plainly but very accurately made. A separate ramrod was used.

69

round them. Loading was greatly simplified by the use of the 'false muzzle' invented in America in 1840 by Alvan Clark. The bore of the barrel was continued in a short detachable portion arranged to fit on in exactly the same position every time. This portion was rifled with the barrel and was then given a taper at the open end so that the tightly fitted bullet could be funnelled into the barrel without damaging the patch or the rifling at the muzzle. The false muzzle was, of course, removed for firing.

A major improvement was made in 1868 by W E Metford, a civil engineer with a keen interest in rifle shooting. Instead of a mechanically fitted bullet, or a soft bullet which was expanded into deep rifling by the powder pressure, he used a fairly hard cylindrical bullet, which had only to expand very slightly into

Left
Short Magazine Lee Enfield with bayonet, sling and dummy rounds. The NRA favoured Army rifles for target shooting until the 1950s.

Below
The butt and lock of a good Pennsylvanian long rifle, made by Jacob Dickert of Lancaster, c.1775–80. It has all the usual features, including brass furniture, but somewhat unusually it has a hair trigger. Such rifles were used for turkey shooting.

shallow rifling. The barrels, being nearly smooth, hardly fouled at all, especially if a greased wad was put behind the bullet, and the bullet itself was a smooth projectile. Another feature he used was rifling which increased in pitch as it went from breech to muzzle – an American idea, although Metford varied the pitch according to a complicated theory of his own. The rifling had the incidental result that it slit the paper patch into strips which separated from the bullet as soon as it left the muzzle instead of sticking to it and affecting its flight. Rigby copied Metford's shallow grooving in his later rifles but used constant-pitch rifling.

The muzzle-loading target rifle remained in use in Britain until about 1878, by which time it was an anachronism, the Army having modified the Enfield to breech-loading in 1867 and having adopted the Martini-Henry in 1871. But the muzzle-loader was more accurate than the early breech-loaders, and was not seriously challenged until about 1874.

In 1874 an event occurred which shook the British shooting establishment to its roots. The British were, at the time, rifle-shooting snobs, happy in the belief that their shooting led the world. In 1873, seeking new fields to conquer, they challenged the Americans to a rifle match by putting

an advertisement in the *New York Herald*. The Americans beat them, despite having little experience in long-range shooting, using breech-loading rifles. The Irish team, who as current holders of the Elcho Shield were representing Britain, all used Rigby muzzle-loaders. Their defeat gave great encouragement to the development of breech-loading target rifles in Britain. Such rifles had had been in use since 1868 but had only recently become competitive with the muzzle-loaders. Almost all were single-shot weapons with falling-block actions such as the Farquharson. Most were .45 (11.43-mm) calibre, shooting paper-patched lead bullets from solid-drawn cases. Metford rifling was popular, but there were numerous other types. Some competitors wiped out the bore of their rifles after every shot. This again was an American idea, and slightly increased accuracy. But the committee of NRA felt that this was going too far and banned the practice in 1883.

The introduction of smokeless powder and jacketed bullets, *ie* bullets with a lead core and a copper or nickel coating, occurred in 1888 with the adoption of the Lee-Metford rifle. Most long-range target shooting was then carried out with these rifles, occasionally with the addition of better sights. Special match rifles continued in use for a

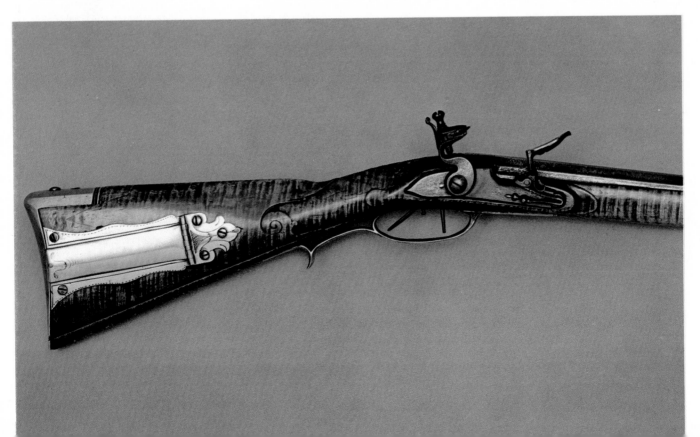

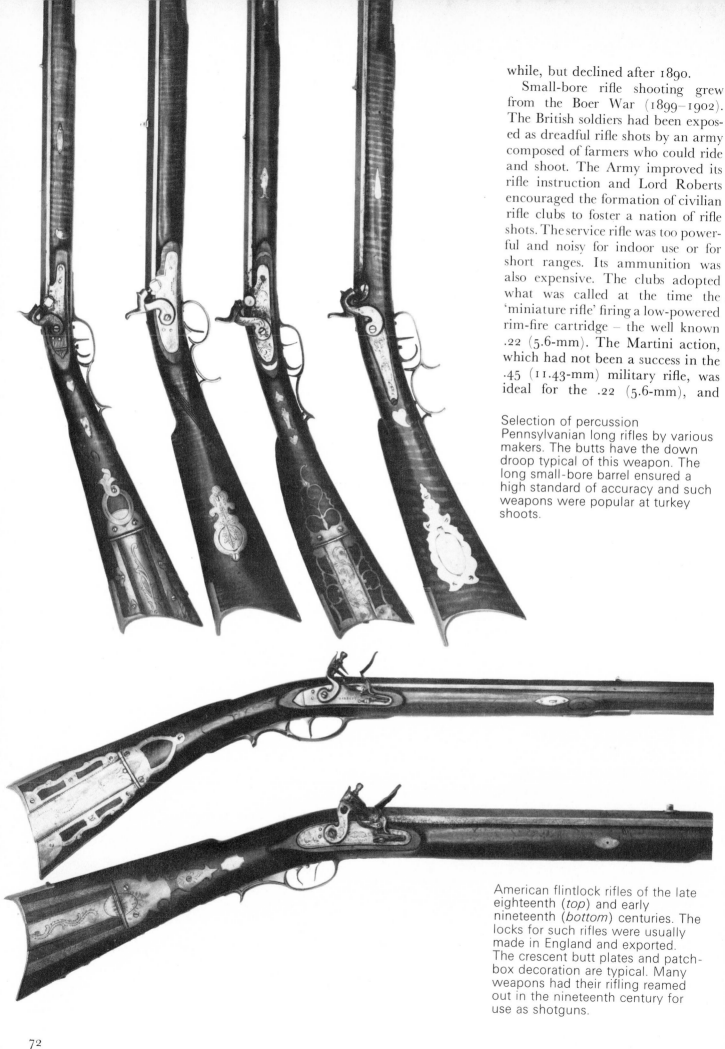

while, but declined after 1890.

Small-bore rifle shooting grew from the Boer War (1899–1902). The British soldiers had been exposed as dreadful rifle shots by an army composed of farmers who could ride and shoot. The Army improved its rifle instruction and Lord Roberts encouraged the formation of civilian rifle clubs to foster a nation of rifle shots. The service rifle was too powerful and noisy for indoor use or for short ranges. Its ammunition was also expensive. The clubs adopted what was called at the time the 'miniature rifle' firing a low-powered rim-fire cartridge – the well known .22 (5.6-mm). The Martini action, which had not been a success in the .45 (11.43-mm) military rifle, was ideal for the .22 (5.6-mm), and

Selection of percussion Pennsylvanian long rifles by various makers. The butts have the down droop typical of this weapon. The long small-bore barrel ensured a high standard of accuracy and such weapons were popular at turkey shoots.

American flintlock rifles of the late eighteenth (*top*) and early nineteenth (*bottom*) centuries. The locks for such rifles were usually made in England and exported. The crescent butt plates and patch-box decoration are typical. Many weapons had their rifling reamed out in the nineteenth century for use as shotguns.

thousands of target rifles were built with it, often by rebarrelling .45 (11.43-mm) rifles.

Most long-range target shooting was carried out with Army rifles until the Army adopted the self-loading rifle in the 1950s. The NRA felt that such rifles were unsuitable for target use, and civilian rifle shots now use heavy-barrelled bolt-action weapons chambered for the 7.62-mm Army service cartridge.

The first rifles specially designed for target use appeared in America in the 1790s, although informal target shooting had been popular for many years. The target was often a live turkey, and was won by the first man to hit it. The rifles were heavy octagonal-barrelled flintlocks with barrels 38–40 in (96.5–101.6 cm) long with hair or 'set' triggers. They fired cloth patched spherical balls, as did all rifles of the period.

About 1835 an improved type of rifle was developed, fitted by this time with the percussion lock. These weapons fired an elongated bullet in a linen patch from heavy barrels which were turned at the muzzle to accept bullet starters which slid on to the muzzle to assist loading. These were not rifled, but merely guided the bullet into the bore. The calibres were small by European standards, usually between .36 in (9.1 mm) and .42 in (10.7 mm), but the rifles were heavy, usually 9–15 lb (4–6.8 kg). The early rifles fired bullets with fairly short cylindrical portions and these had to be accurately centred in the bore for successful results. The poor powder probably expanded the bullet very little, and the makers found that gaining twist rifling gave better accuracy, perhaps by reducing the bullet's chances of stripping.

In 1840 Clark invented the false muzzle already described, and by this means long, tightly fitted bullets in paper patches could be inserted into the bore. The increase in accuracy was considerable. Heavy target rifles, fired from a rest and fitted with telescopic sights were capable of shooting 2½-in (6.35-cm) groups at 220 yd (201 m). Rifles of this type, sometimes with telescopic sights, were used to good effect for sniping by Colonel Berdan's regiment of sharpshooters in the American Civil War. They were last used around 1880.

The introduction of long-range target rifles in the United States has a curious history. The National Rifle Association of America was formed in 1871 and built a range at Creedmore, near New York. In 1873, as described earlier, the Irish rifle team advertised a challenge in the *New York Herald*. Since it was not addressed to the NRAA, they did not take up the challenge, but the Amateur Rifle Club of New York City did. Long-range shooting was not practised at the time in the United States and no member of the team had ever fired at over 500 yd (457 m), nor did suitable rifles exist for them to do so.

The Sharps and Remington companies were asked to produce long-range breech-loading target rifles at short notice, and succeeded in doing so by improving their powerful rifles used for hunting buffalo. The team practised at Creedmore at 800, 900 and 1,000 yd (731, 823 and 914 m). Three Remington and three Sharps rifles were used, all firing .44-in (11.18-mm) bullets weighing 550 grains with 90–95 grains of powder.

The match was shot in 1874. The Americans won but it was a close

thing. Factors that contributed to their success were the use of the back position for shooting, which was little used in Britain, and the custom of wiping out their bores between each shot, an action made easy by the breech-loading weapons. Tremendous public interest attended the match. Similar rifles to those used were sold by the makers in fair numbers, but even so long-range rifle shooting never really become popular in America. Ranges were difficult to build, the rifles were expensive, and their recoil was heavy. Instead, short-range shooting on the Continental plan became popular from about 1880 onwards, fostered by the large number of German and Swiss immigrants. A cartridge firing a .38 (9.7-mm) bullet with 55 grains of powder was widely used.

With the adoption of metallic cartridges and the use of breech-loading rifles, the sport of target shooting became more and more technically complicated. There were numerous experiments combining different actions, calibres and stocks, and sights of various styles were adopted, but there have been no innovations of real importance and the rifles are basically unchanged, except in quality, from those of 50 years ago.

A modern stalking rifle with a pistol grip and a firmly mounted telescope. It is a bolt-action, magazine weapon.

Military Weapons

David Penn

During the eighteenth century no European state had both the financial ability and the desire to indulge in superfluous military investment. Armies were no larger than was deemed to be necessary for the survival of the state. The soldier was almost always a highly trained, if poorly paid, professional. He was thus hard to replace and a prized commodity not to be sacrificed lightly. Both the soldier and his equipment were expected to last a long time, but if two such well disciplined professional armies joined battle, they could effect considerable damage to one another.

Battles were bloody affairs, and losses tended to be heavy, not only because of the primitive state of medicine but because professional armies were trained to 'slug it out' at relatively close range, fire being held until the enemy was within effective musketry range, about 80–120 yd (73–110 m). Because volley fire under orders lessens the individual feeling of responsibility for homicide, because the troops were trained, and because they were themselves subjected to real danger from the enemy, the troops were motivated to engage their opponents as effectively as possible.

There was little point in giving all eighteenth-century soldiers a rifle, since a rifle took up to three times as long to load as a musket, leaving its user at a strong disadvantage after the first shot. Rifles tended to remain as specialist arms in the hands of elite and mobile light troops who were used for scouting, skirmishing, ambushes and sniping at officers.

It was nonetheless recognized that a rifle that could shoot as fast as a musket or a breech-loader, and could be reloaded faster, would be a real advantage, and several nations made serious attempts to solve the design problems involved. A principal cause of the trouble was the thick, caked soot caused by firing black powder, and significant improvements in powder technology in the eighteenth century reduced its sootiness only a

The inaccuracy of the eighteenth-century musket was demonstrated at a military execution of three Highland Scots at the Tower of London in July 1743. Despite the efforts at short range of a squad of 12 men, two of the victims had to be given the *coup de grâce*.

Saxon infantry in 1859 carrying out
volley fire — an important part of
eighteenth- and nineteenth-century
warfare techniques. Much time was
spent in practising the repeated
volley, firing by rank after rank.

Above
This Brown Bess musket has the 46-in (122-cm) barrel; the lock is marked 'GOVERS' and bears the date '1760'. The barrel is engraved '62nd REGT'. It could well have seen service during the American War of Independence (1775–83) for the regiment served there and surrendered at Saratoga.

Below
A somewhat romantic impression of the unfortunate incident known as the Boston Massacre, when British troops were provoked into firing on an unruly crowd in Boston, Massachusetts on 3 March 1770. Three citizens were killed and two were mortally wounded.

Right
One of a series of eighteenth-century French engravings depicting the story of the American War of Independence. This one shows the opening Battle of Lexington, fought in April 1775.

Below right
French engraving showing the surrender of Lord Cornwallis in October 1781 after the Siege of Yorktown, which effectively ended the war. In the background troops are stacking their Brown Bess muskets.

Below
Soldier of the late eighteenth century with a poorly delineated Brown Bess musket. The cross belts support his cartridge box and bayonet.

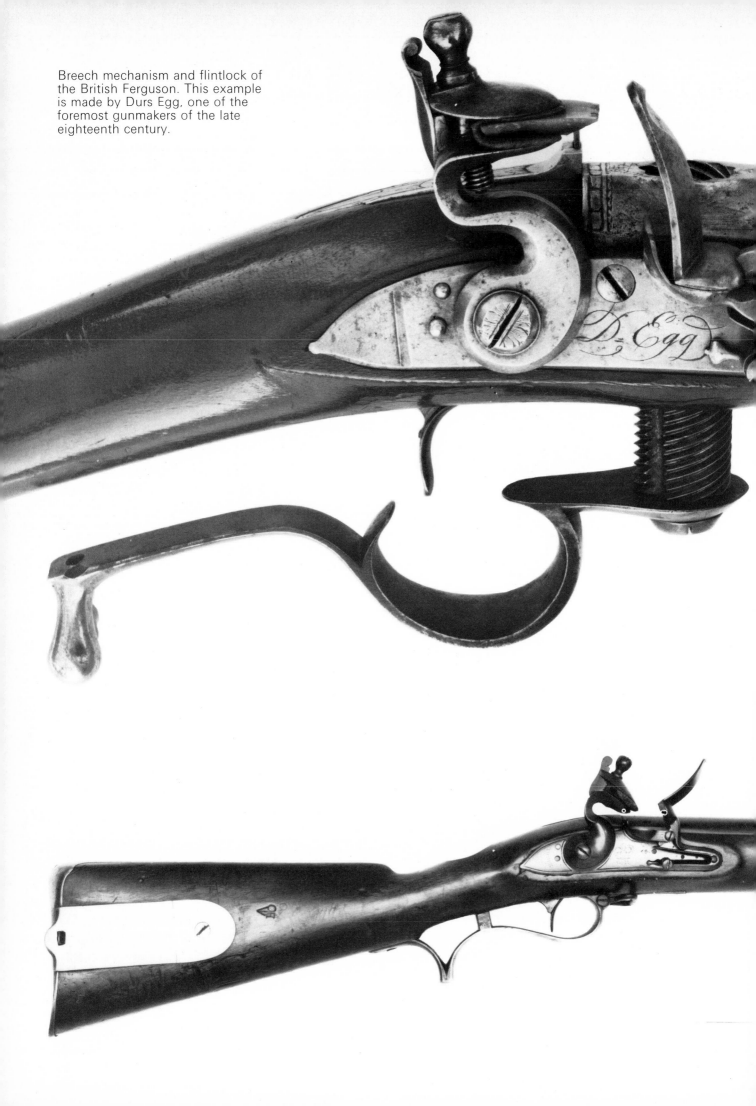

Breech mechanism and flintlock of the British Ferguson. This example is made by Durs Egg, one of the foremost gunmakers of the late eighteenth century.

little. These deposits made it progressively harder to ram down a tightly fitting projectile. The problem could be minimized in a smooth-bore musket by supplying an undersized ball and sacrificing accuracy for speed of fire. The raison d'être of a rifle is accuracy, however, and a ball had to fit the rifling closely. The ballistic technology of the time only allowed three solutions: to use an undersized ball with a lubricated patch, as in the American Kentucky rifle, which alleviated but did not solve the problem; or to load at the breech, or to abandon black powder entirely and adopt an air weapon.

There were two main approaches to the military breech-loader in the eighteenth century. One was the hinged breech used in the Austrian Crespi, a smooth-bored weapon introduced on a limited scale in 1770. In this system, a section of the barrel at the breech was hinged so that it could be pivoted upwards and loaded with a paper cartridge. After a short time the hinged breech was withdrawn (in 1777) because it leaked gas in a disconcerting fashion, occasionally dangerous to the shooter. The idea was revived with equal lack of success by Durs Egg, a London gunmaker, as a rifled carbine for British Light Dragoons, who appear to have used them only between 1786 and '88. The alternative was a screw plug that transversed the barrel behind the chamber. This system, probably invented by John Willmore and improved by Isaac de la Chaumette, was reasonably gas-tight, but demanded close tolerances in manufacture. It was further modified by a Scot, Captain Patrick Ferguson, who introduced a modified screw thread and plug that reduced the effects of fouling. Ferguson, a fine shot, demonstrated the wet-weather capabilities and accuracy of his rifle at up to 200 yd (183 m) at Woolwich in 1776, making sufficient impression on his audience to secure permission to equip a light corps in America under

Left
This engraving was the frontispiece of a famous nineteenth-century book on rifles and shooting, entitled *Scloppetaria* and written by Captain Henry Beaufoy. The rifleman is shooting a Baker-type rifle.

Far left
Butt and lock of a Baker rifle. The brass cover at the end of the butt covers a cavity which housed waxed patches used when loading the rifle.

Right
This Austrian hussar of 1806 carries his carbine slung on a shoulder strap with a large spring swivel. Most of the cavalry at this period used similar methods.

Below
French camp of Napoleon I. The guards have stacked their flintlock muskets, and several have their locks wrapped to keep them dry. Musée de l'Armée, Paris.

his command with 300 of his rifles. A brilliant anti-guerrilla leader, his successes against the rebellious colonists resulted in the extermination of his unit and his own death at the hands of an American force three times its size at King's Mountain in 1780. No further interest was shown in his rifle on the grounds that it was too difficult to make and too expensive to be suitable for wider issue.

The ever-inventive Austrians also issued a repeating pneumatic air rifle, the Girandoni. This used the butt as a reservoir for compressed air, good for 20–40 shots, and a 20-round magazine, giving it the amazing rate of fire of 20 shots in 20 seconds. Girandoni's air rifle was effective only to about 100 yd (91 m), producing about the same performance as a modern .45 Colt revolver cartridge, but its speed of fire and lack of all-enveloping smoke were strong advantages. Against them weighed the weapon's extreme expense, the expertise needed to make them, the impossibility of repair in the field for the fragile valve system, and the need for 2,000 strokes of a pump to recharge a butt with air.

In truth, however, these breechloaders and air weapons were militarily insignificant. All armies relied on a smooth-bore musket as their general-issue infantry weapon, some also issuing a muzzle-loading rifle for special purposes. Cavalry, if they carried firearms at all, were provided with smooth-bore pistols or simple carbines.

The first major attempt at change was not in the design of the muzzle-loading weapons themselves, but in methods of manufacture. Although the French by 1785 had made the first hesitant steps towards mass production using unskilled labour, the initiative was stifled by the requirement for vast numbers of muskets generated by Napoleon I's military policies. The Revolution had crippled the army of the *Ancien Régime*, and Napoleon had no option but to introduce the concept of the *levée en masse*, huge, ill-trained but fast-moving conscript armies fighting with at least an intermittent patriotic fervour. Not only did the ability of the individual soldier decline, but he was worse armed than his predecessor. Hand manufacture on a piecework basis required skilled craftsmen with years of experience, and inevitably the need for quantity caused a real decline in quality in both French and English muskets of the period.

In England, the Short Land Pattern was supplemented after 1795 by

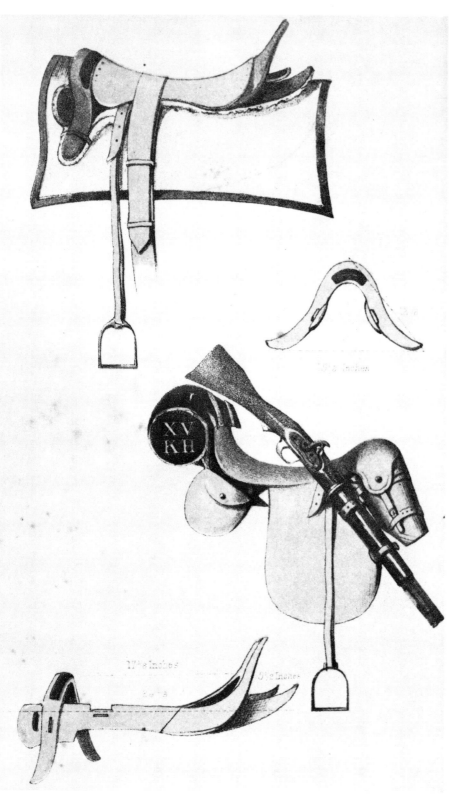

Details of the horse furniture of the 15th (The King's) Hussars. Here the carbine has a special scabbard fitted by the side of the saddle together with the pistol holsters.

CAPTURE OF CHIN-KEANG-FOO.

Above
British infantry go into the attack during the China War of 1842 to capture Chin-Keang-Foo. Percussion weapons were by now in the hands of most troops.

Right
One of the best of the military percussion rifles of the mid nineteenth century was the .577 (14.6-mm) British Enfield, here shown with bayonet, shako, and water bottle of the period.

Left
This light infantryman of the North York Militia is shown loading his Baker rifle in 1814. The detail is sketchy but the extended brass trigger guard is clearly indicated.

large quantities of cheaper, simpler India Pattern muskets. The solution in both countries was to expand the existing system by letting out additional contracts to more and more civilian gunmakers. This resulted in continuous rows over prices and quality control, and as early as 1794, the Board of Ordnance saw the proper solution to be a Government manufactory large enough to produce adequate emergency reserves of arms and to 'become a Cheque upon the proceedings of the Gunmakers and prevent Combinations among them against Government'. Such a

factory was erected at Lewisham in 1806, and it did make use of steam-powered lathes and grinders, but it still operated essentially a handwork system, and did not much affect arms supplies during the whole of the Napoleonic campaigns.

Society was changing very quickly by the end of the Napoleonic Wars. An emergent European and American middle class was aggressively materialist and increasingly nationalist. It was determined to make its way in trade and industry. Any man who could exploit cheap unskilled labour by introducing high-volume

production at low unit cost could seriously challenge the skilled artisan. In such a climate, modifications to improve the soldier's firearm and the means of its production were becoming ever more practicable.

There had to be an appropriate conjunction of need, capital and capability, however, or a brilliant design could die unrecognized, as did Samuel Johannes Pauly's breech-loader of 1812. This was a single or double-barrelled weapon firing a completely self-contained cartridge. The body of the cartridge was of paper, and was consumed at the

Breech mechanism of the American Hall rifle, the block raised to receive a paper cartridge. This breech could be detached and carried loaded as a makeshift pistol. The upper jaw of the cock is missing on this example.

moment of firing. Ignition was by means of a disk of fulminate attached to the brass base of the cartridge, and was struck by a short needle. The weapon was a true centre-fire capable of a rate of fire of approximately 11 rounds per minute, three times as fast as a well-handled musket, and in 1815 was demonstrated to Napoleon I's representatives by its Swiss inventor. Militarily it was a nonstarter. The precise fitting required to achieve a gas-tight seal at the breech could not be achieved cheaply or in quantity. The costs of the arms and the fulminate would have been too high for France's wartime economy to bear. France was not yet ready for her breech-loader, and Pauly's gun was relegated, or elevated, to the status of gentleman's plaything. As Napoleon III later wrote, 'Inventions that are before their age remain useless until the stock of general knowledge comes up to their level.'

The stock of general knowledge did not catch up with Pauly until 1842, in Prussia. The Americans, meanwhile, had introduced the Hall in 1819, although production rifles were not issued until 1824. This was a lineal descendant of the Crespi and the Egg, but was a little easier to make. Being a rifle, it outperformed contemporary muskets, and it served with distinction in the Seminole (1835–42) and Mexican Wars (1846–48). It was only a limited-issue arm, and it still leaked gas but not as badly as the Crespi.

The introduction of the percussion system of ignition and of superior projectiles, described in Chapter 1, combined with improved manufacturing techniques, gave the armies of the 1830s and '40s a very difficult choice. They could mass-produce an efficient, simple muzzle-loading rifle with good combat accuracy at six times the range of a smooth-bore musket, or they could risk adopting an unproven breech-loader. The British and the Americans chose to concentrate on mass production, and evolved the British Pattern 1853 .577 (14.47-mm) Enfield and the American 1856 .58 (14.73-mm) Springfield, two essentially identical muzzle-loading arms

Russian Lancers of the Guard at the
time of the Crimean War (1853–56)
were armed with pistols and a
carbine which was hung from a
broad belt going across the shoulder.
A large spring clip engaged with a
loop and bar fitted to the stock of
the carbine.

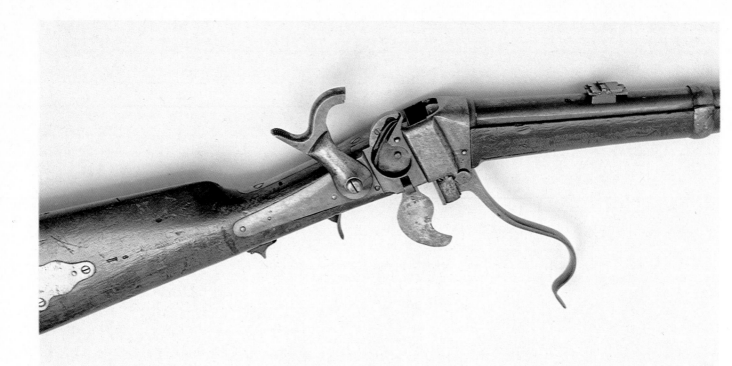

Left
Sharps rifle with action open, ready to receive its combustible cartridge. There was considerable gas loss between barrel and breech face.

Below left
This painting by Manet of the execution of the Emperor Maximilian of Mexico in 1867 clearly shows the percussion rifles used by the soldiers. Städtische Kunsthalle, Mannheim.

Right
This close-up of the open bolt of the German Dreyse needle rifle clearly shows the long, thin needle that had to pierce the combustible cartridge, penetrate the powder charge, and eventually strike the ignition cap placed on the base of the bullet's sabot. Imperial War Museum, London.

Below
Needle rifles. The upper weapon is a Dreyse Model 1841, the original needle-gun. The lower weapon appears to be a German Dorsch & von Baumgarten (1862 patent) Jäger rifle, patterned on the Prussian Model 1865.

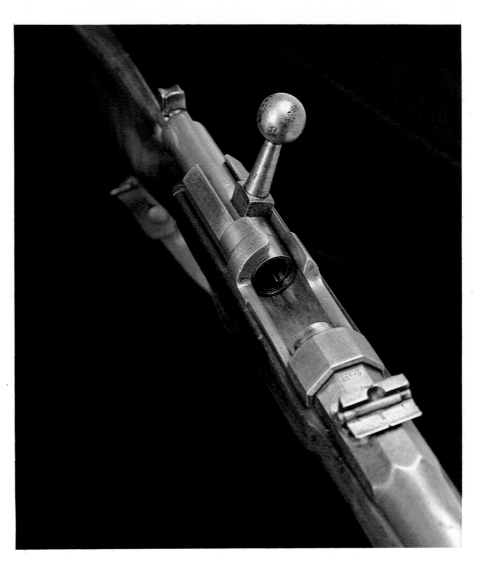

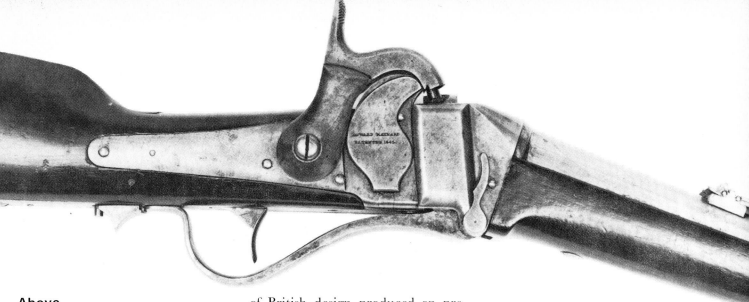

Above
American Sharps capping breech-loader. This version, given limited issue to British cavalry, is fitted with a Maynard tape primer, essentially identical to a roll of paper caps for a child's toy pistol. This device worked well, and was a particular boon for cavalry, since the shooter did not have to position a tiny copper cap on the carbine's nipple before each shot.

Top left
Model 1861 Springfield rifle – the standard weapon of the Federal Army during the American Civil War (1861–65). It was simple but effective and fired a .58-in (14.7-mm) bullet at about 2–3 shots a minute. Winchester Gun Museum, New Haven, Connecticut.

Centre left
A dead Confederate soldier at Petersburg, Virginia lies with an Enfield rifle. Both sides used this British weapon extensively, although this example is probably the photographer Matthew Brady's own 'prop' rifle.

Left
This group of US Civil War infantry bivouac with their Springfield rifles in the stack or pile position.

of British design produced on predominantly American machine tools.

The manufacturing processes were controlled and checked to a high degree, and a complex production line represented a very heavy capital investment. At this period mass production entailed the loss of flexibility of the old hand-worker. There was thus every disincentive to change, once the rifles were adopted. It should not be thought that the British Army was insensitive to the faults of the muzzle-loader. It was readily admitted that it was slow to load, very hard to reload lying down. or while running or on a horse, and required at least one violent movement to ram down a cartridge, which made concealment difficult. Worse, in the heat of battle it was all too easy either to insert the ball before the powder, putting the weapon out of action, or to forget that it was loaded and to ram a second charge on top. This happened with surprising frequency in the hands of green troops. After Gettysburg (1863), over 37,000 rifles were picked up. Nearly 8,000 were double-loaded and 6,000 had three or more loads. One rifle contained 23! The difficulty of reloading also encouraged many soldiers not immediately under their officers' eyes to refrain from firing their weapon, and to conserve their single shot in anticipation of more pressing personal danger.

The British were aware that the weak copper-cased rim-fire and pin-fire metallic cartridges of the 1850s were not immediately capable of development to produce an effective high-powered rifle. So far as breech-loading military arms were con-

American Union soldier of Berdan's Sharpshooters reaches for a paper cartridge to reload his muzzle-loading rifle, an awkward business when kneeling behind cover.

cerned, the choice in the 1850s was between a needle-fire self-contained cartridge and a capping breech-loader, in which a paper, skin or linen cartridge was ignited by a separate percussion cap or tape primer. Of all the capping breech-loaders tested in England, only the Westley Richards 'monkey tail' was reasonably gas-tight. It was an excellent arm, and achieved a distinguished reputation as a sporting and colonial military weapon. Infantry breech-loading designs by Callow, Kufhal, Malherbe, Melville and Montigny, along with the German Dreyse needle-gun, were also tested between 1849 and 1851. All of them were finally rejected in

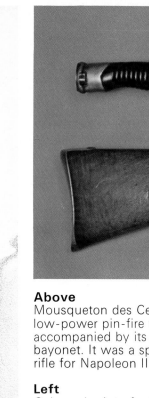

favour of an improved muzzle-
loader.

The Dreyse, however, had been
adopted as a general issue infantry
rifle by Prussia in 1842. Johann
Dreyse had been apprenticed to
Pauly in Paris, and had continued to
work on a self-contained combustible
cartridge detonated by a needle. By
1835 this had been developed into a
recognizable turn-bolt action, which
fired an egg-shaped projectile, a
more stable form than a round ball,
but which was undersized and held
in a papier-maché sabot, which also
supported the percussion cap. A long
fragile needle had to punch right
through the paper case and powder
charge to ignite the cap. The failure
rate of needles was high, roughly the
same as of a good gun flint, and each
soldier was equipped with two spares.

The weapon leaked gas horribly at
the breech since there was no effective seal. The rate of manufacture was
also very slow, and the weapon was
only issued in reasonable numbers in
time for the wars against Denmark in
1864 and the Seven Weeks' War
against Austria in 1866. Both were
signal Prussian victories, and Europe's press focussed on the needle-
gun as a major contributor to this
success. This was certainly a simplis-
tic interpretation but the breech-
loader again became a matter of
intense concern to the military mind.

Faced with the need for parity
with Prussia, England sought an
easy means of converting its large
stocks of .577 (14.47-mm) Enfields
to breech-loaders. After it had become clear that adequate supplies of
combustible skin cartridges could not
be guaranteed for the Montgomery-
Storm, the system originally selected,
Colonel Boxer, the Superintendent
of the Royal Laboratories, then suggested that the side-hinged breech-
block conversion submitted to the
trials by an American, Jacob Snider,
should be adopted, along with his
own modifications to the Snider
cartridge which rendered this rather
unsatisfactory cardboard-bodied design both practicable, cheap and
easily made. The Snider was simple,
economical, costing about £1 to
convert each rifle, and very strong.
The original lock, stock and barrel
were retained but the barrel was
modified by being slightly shortened,
having a chamber reamed at its
rear end, and being threaded into

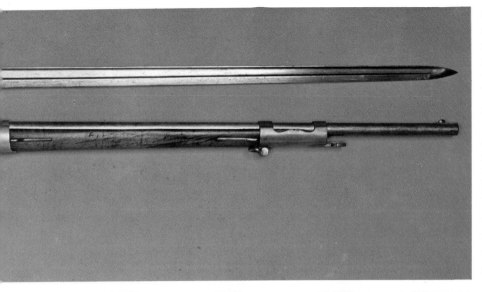

the Snider action. The high quality of the original rifle and the sound engineering of the action ensured a long, honourable and relatively trouble-free service life up to World War I, when it was still in the hands of some cadets and colonial units.

The Boxer cartridge was really a development of the French Pottet and Schneider patents, in which the priming compound was held neither in the rim, nor as a cap under a pin, but as a cap located in the centre of the base of the cartridge: the 'centre-fire'. Boxer's cartridge was made up of an iron base to which was riveted a brass tube coiled by hand. Although by no means as strong as a modern solid-drawn brass cartridge, the Boxer round was cheap and it provided a fully effective gas seal. A modification in bullet design, incorporating an idea of one of the great British engineers, William Ellis Metford, in which a hollow was incorporated into the nose as well as the base of the bullet, to give better weight distribution, contributed to a worthwhile gain in accuracy over the Enfield.

At last there existed a gas-tight, trouble-free breech-loader that improved on the long-range performance of the best muzzle-loaders, could outshoot the Prussian needle-gun, and was mercifully cheap. The Turks, Serbs, Montenegrins and Portuguese all opted for the Snider conversion, and a flood of other hinged-breech conversion systems appeared in stiff competition with one another.

There were three main approaches. The first, the side-hinged

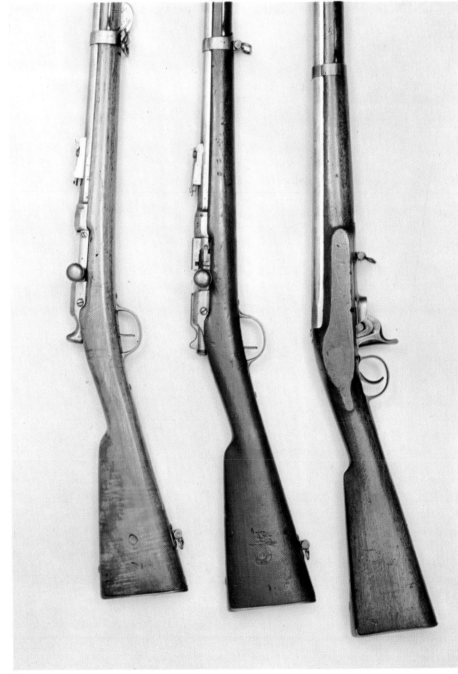

From left to right
The French Chassepot of 1866, which fired an 11-mm combustible cartridge. Before the bolt could be withdrawn, the large cocking-piece at the rear had to be pulled back. Next is the much more efficient metallic-cartridge Gras. This began life as a Chassepot conversion, but some were again converted to 8-mm in 1914, and issued to second-line troops.
Heurteloup's rifled musket of 1834—44. This weapon employs an under-hammer system and a tube primer.
Pattern Room, Royal Small Arms Factory, Enfield.

block, was at its best in the Snider; other side-swing patterns were the Austrian Krnka, adopted by Russia, the Bonin, Schneider and 'Tabatière'; this last French design was named after a fancied resemblance to the hinge-lidded metal snuffboxes of the period. The second approach was to have an elevating breechblock hinged at the front. Examples are the American Berdan I adopted in 1867 by Spain and Russia; the Allin, named after the American Superintendent of Springfield Armoury, selected in 1868 to convert Springfield rifle-muskets, and established as being a patent infringement of Berdan's device; the Swiss Milbank-Amsler, adopted in 1868; the Austrian Wanzl of 1866, and the Albini-Braendlin, designed in Italy, made in Birmingham and issued in Belgium.

The third variety of block was hinged at the rear, such as the Restell and the Needham, and was least popular of these designs since it possessed no mechanical advantages. Innumerable other conversion systems of a greater or lesser degree of complexity, economy and practability were touted by the gunsmiths of Europe, fine collections of which exist in the Musée des Armes in Liège and in the Vatican.

While most of Europe was rushing to convert its muzzle-loaders to simple metallic cartridge-firing breech-loaders, the French were poised to upset the ammunition cart again and touch off a whole new arms race. After a brief flirtation with the Snider they took the apparently retrogressive step of introducing in 1866 a new bolt-action needle-gun designed by Alphonse Antoine Chassepot. This has generally been ascribed to a desire to ape Prussian success, but it was really nothing of the kind. The French believed that they had not only nullified the disadvantages of the Dreyse but had designed a new cartridge that would significantly outperform anything else in Europe, and would have an effective range 90% in excess of the ageing Dreyse's.

The main criterion of a successful military rifle is not pinpoint accuracy, but its ability to strike a man somewhere between the top of his head and his foot when aimed at his stomach. If the bullet moves slowly and the trajectory is high this 'danger zone' or 'point blank range' is very short, since, unless range is estimated precisely, the bullet will go over the top of the target's head if the shooter seriously overestimates the range, or will strike the ground in front of him if the shooter underestimates. This puts a premium on precise range estimation, accurate sight adjustment and a cool head in battle. If however, the rifle shoots sufficiently flat for a single sight-setting to ensure a hit over a very long 'point blank range' of several hundred yards, the soldier has no need of the skills of either range estimation or of sight adjustment.

The Chassepot employed a .43 (10.9 mm) bore, a rather oversize bullet of 386 grains and a hefty powder charge of 85 grains. This should have achieved about a 20% flatter trajectory than the Snider, while employing a combustible cartridge weighing only two-thirds as much. Instead of a long thin Dreyse needle, a short striker was employed to detonate a cap placed within the rear wad of the cartridge. Some authorities indeed maintain that a Chassepot is not a needle rifle at all, but a combustible centre-fire. This certainly reduced the chances of needle breakage, but the Chassepot was notorious for squirting hot gas back along the firing pin channel towards the firer's eye. The French were convinced that they had solved the problem of sealing the breech against gas escape by incorporating an India-rubber seal in the bolt. This worked for a few rounds, but the heat soon vulcanized the rubber seal and rendered it useless.

The Chassepot's potential, if not actual, performance could not be ignored. The armies of Europe, or at least those of the Great Powers, were forced to abandon their cosy round of testing, discussing and then shelving or rejecting new rifle designs, and get to grips with the vexatious problem of introducing a new rifle of improved performance.

With the advantage of hindsight, and a greater familiarity with the

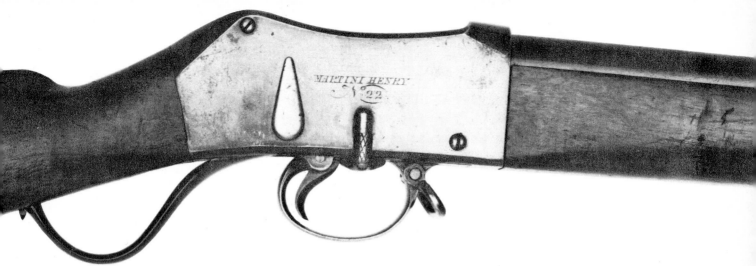

A prototype Martini-Henry used for acceptance tests. The tear-drop-shaped device indicates whether the striker is cocked or at rest. The cross-hatched catch in front of the trigger is a safety catch, omitted in the production rifle.

The open breech of the Soper rifle. This example is a very late .303 Metford rifled sporting rifle of *c* 1900, and is still in an unfinished condition. The metal work has not been polished and the stock is still in the rough. Clifford Owen Collection.

performance of well-developed, safe, trouble-free twentieth-century fire-arms, historians have tended to underestimate the very real difficulties of Ordnance Boards faced with, in some cases, over 100 untried, even experimental, rifle designs and new methods of ammunition construction. In the light of the military history of the later nineteenth century, a bolt-action would have seemed by far the most logical military choice for the 1860s, being cheap, simple, strong, and easy to convert to a repeater.

The picture looked very different in the 1860s, however. Early bolt-actions, particularly the Chassepot, had a justifiably bad reputation for premature ignition which was potentially extremely dangerous to the operator. The bolt-action is quite violent in its action, being briskly slammed shut in operation, while most other single-shot actions required that the cartridge be fully chambered with the fingers, a gentle means of loading that minimized any risk through fragile or faulty cartridges or because of chamber obstruction.

At a period of rapid technical innovation, it was inevitable that the action, barrel and cartridge of a rifle submitted for testing might differ widely in their efficiency. An excellent action system might thus be overlooked because it was coupled with a militarily unacceptable type of cartridge.

The British trials for a new breech-loader began in October 1866, and 104 designs were submitted. The Swiss-American Martini action was eventually adopted in 1869, fitted with a Henry-pattern barrel. This was a hammerless rifle designed by Frederick von Martini as a modification of the hammer-fired Peabody with a block hinged at the rear and operated by an underlever. It had an exceptionally fast lock time, was very strong, and was relatively simple to make. Many contemporary experts considered it by no means the best choice, however.

The Martini-Henry was capable of 40 rounds a minute if it did not jam, as opposed to the Chassepot's 19 and the Dreyse's 9. Its main drawback was its weak extraction, exacerbated by the continued use of the Boxer type of coiled brass case, which, when applied to the high-pressure bottle-necked .577/.450 case, was prone to stick in the chamber, especially in very hot conditions. This caused a major outcry during the Sudanese Campaign of 1884–5. At Abu Klea, Gubat and Abu Kroo, many rifles jammed at the first or second volley, and an average of 33 per cent of rifles were out of action during the first engagement.

The alternative system of case construction employed a single piece of brass, drawn out by machinery. Both the cartridge case and its means of production were the invention in 1870 of the prolific American designer and marksman, Colonel Hiram Berdan. This construction was much sturdier than the Boxer case, and contracted much more reliably after firing, thus minimizing the danger of sticking in the chamber. The British Army was well aware of the virtues of the Berdan case, adopting it almost immediately for Gardner and Gatling machine guns, but, despite the

Left
The American 'Trapdoor' Springfield. This system, designed by Allin, was intended to be a conversion system for muzzle-loaders. Although not very strong, and lacking powerful extraction, the single-shot Springfield was the main army rifle of the frontier Indian Wars, and was still in service in militia hands in 1898, during the Spanish-American War. Imperial War Museum, London.

Right
Remington Rolling Block. This American design was simple, economical and very popular. It was the foundation of Remington's wide success as an international military arms supplier. Imperial War Museum, London.

Berdan's widespread issue in Europe, did not officially phase out the coiled case for foreign use in rifles until 1888.

The European powers were stumbling around in much the same way, seeking an improvement on their muzzle-loading conversions. Russia adopted in 1868 the hinged-breech Berdan I, another brainchild of the American general, chambered for a .42 (10.7-mm) cartridge ballistically superior to the Martini-Henry's. The first 90,000 were made by Colt, but subsequent production was based on the Russian state arsenal at Tula. The Berdan I was prone to premature discharge as it did not have a retracting firing pin, and was superseded by the Berdan II in 1871, a bolt-action using the same cartridge, built at Tula on British-made Greenwood and Batley machinery installed under American supervision.

Despite close study of the Früwirth repeater, Austria adopted the Werndl, an 11.15-mm Steyr-designed rifle chosen in the face of stiff American competition from the Peabody and a Remington design, of which more below. Turkey was buying American Peabody and Peabody-Martini single-shot designs from 1869 onwards, but supplementing them with American Spencer and Winchester repeaters. The Peabody design preceded the Martini, and in some ways was superior to it. It enjoyed some vogue in Europe as a sort of stop-gap or substitute arm, being bought in

significant quantities by Switzerland, Rumania, Cuba, Mexico, Denmark and, in 1870, by an embattled France. A much-modified Peabody-Martini action was adopted by Bavaria as the Werder.

In 1867–70, the main competitor to the hinged-block or falling-block rifle was another single-shot design, the Remington Rolling Block, stemming from an 1863 patent of Leonard Geiger, but extensively modified in 1866. This action was of a wonderful simplicity, the breech-block being hinged below the line of the barrel, and locked in place at the moment of firing by the shaped underpiece of the hammer. This is not a particularly strong action, but it was adequate for the cartridges of the day, and was reliable and trouble-free in use. In 1867 the Remington was adopted by the US Navy, at which point there was considerable but unsuccessful Royal Navy agitation to acquire 'Rimingtons', as they called them, in preference to Sniders. Remington, an aggressive salesman, presented convincing arguments to those countries that could not afford exhaustive testing or were not overburdened by chauvinism. The system was adopted in 1867 by Denmark, in 1868 by Sweden and Norway, in 1869 by Cuba and Spain, and by Egypt in 1870. Substantial quantities were also sold to Greece, China, France and in South America.

The Papal States used the Remington, but had it made by the old Catholic gunmaking house of Nagant Frères in Belgium. The Pope's personal bodyguards were armed with magnificent specimens, fitted with

Above
Private John Warrick, Berkshire Volunteers, firing his .577/.450 Soper at Wimbledon, probably in 1872. The Soper was considered by many to be a far superior military rifle to the Martini-Henry, although it was more complex and expensive. Fired in this supine position, it could achieve the astounding rate of fire of 60 shots a minute. Warrick was one of Soper's gunsmiths, and the best military rifle shot in England. L. Matthews Collection.

Right
The Franco-Prussian War of 1870–71 led to the setting up of a Paris Commune. There was much confused fighting and this is a typical 'heroic' engraving of the period. Entitled *A la mort*, the fighters move forward armed with Chassepot rifles and bayonets. The artist's licence is considerable, as Chassepots were not equipped with this type of socket bayonet.

silver-plated actions, Damascus twist barrels, and finely figured walnut stocks, each one being paid for by one of the noble Catholic houses of Europe! The rolling block, modified in 1896–97 and 1902, made a successful transition to modern high-velocity smokeless cartridges, being adopted in 7-mm by Mexico. Even the Royal Navy finally got its own way, 48 years too late, buying up stocks of 7-mm versions in 1914 to arm fishing vessels against U-boats and mines.

If 1866–70 was the 'block age',

1871 was the year of the bolt. Prussia had beaten France in 1870 while still armed with her obsolete Dreyse, but had realized that reputation alone was not enough justification for the retention of the leaky old horror, especially as the French had tried to buy themselves out of trouble by acquiring large quantities of excellent American breech-loaders. The Prussians adopted the Mauser 11-mm single-shot bolt-action in 1871. This was based on the Württemberger, Peter Paul Mauser's American patent of 1868, in which

the Remington company had had an interest. Mauser's action, which had already been unsuccessfully offered to the French as a means of converting the Chassepot to metallic cartridges, was a major improvement on earlier bolt designs. It incorporated a 'cock-on-opening' feature which withdrew the firing pin as the bolt handle was lifted and removed the danger of accidental discharge on closing which had so bedevilled earlier designs. The arm became an instant success, was issued widely, if not quite universally by the German

States, and saw much use in China and Japan. The Dutch introduced the Beaumont, an inferior design with the firing pin powered by a 'V' spring incorporated into the bolt handle, and the Italians the Swiss Vetterli, but as a single-shot design rather than as a repeater. The Vetterli was a good action, but over-large and ugly.

France in 1874 adopted a metallic cartridge conversion of the Chassepot, designed by General Bertile Gras. This weapon turned out to be quite satisfactory in service and so, with the arms balance restored, Europe settled back into peaceful small-scale experimentation for another decade, with the emphasis on repeaters.

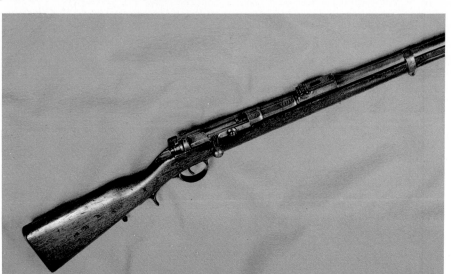

Above left
British Grenadier Guardsman with his Martini-Henry rifle in about 1885. He wears medals for the Egyptian campaign of 1882.

Left
German Model 1871 rifle. This version is the slightly shorter Jäger rifle. Imperial War Museum, London.

Repeating Weapons

David Penn

The search for an efficient repeating rifle went hand-in-hand with the development of the self-contained metallic cartridge and techniques of volume cartridge manufacture and military supply.

On a 'shots per casualty' ratio, we see a steady decline in efficiency from the mid-eighteenth century to the present day. It seems that during the first volley or two of an eighteenth-century battle, when discipline and order still held and the enemy was unobscured by smoke, a well-trained unit would achieve up to 1 hit for every 5 musket balls fired. By the Napoleonic Wars, the hit rate was down to about 1 for 20. In some American Civil War battles, it appears that about 200 rounds needed to be fired to cause a casualty.

The muzzle-loader could attain a great concentration of fire by being fired en masse and in volley. There American repeaters. At the top is the Model '03 Springfield, the official American service rifle in World War I. In the middle is the 12-gauge Winchester Model 97 military shotgun, capable of taking the Springfield bayonet. At the bottom is the excellent US-made, British-designed Enfield Model 1917, a substitute standard arm that was eventually issued in greater numbers than the Springfield. Imperial War Museum, London.

Above
Early example of a multi-chambered gun, *circa* 1620–30. The cylinder held five charges and had to be rotated by hand to bring each into position for firing. Musée de l'Armée, Paris.

Right and below
Two views of a flintlock revolving rifle by E. H. Collier of London, patented in 1818. It was a five-shot weapon, the cylinder being rotated by hand to bring each chamber in line with the barrel.

was then a long pause for reloading, during which any surviving enemy troops were safe to move around. A single-shot breech-loader could also produce the same concentrated effect, but the speed of reloading greatly cut down the 'safe period'. A repeater reduced still further this brief respite and thus limited the opposition's opportunity for any kind of movement.

While industrialized nations with large populations were able to sustain heavy losses without capitulation, and to replace fallen troops with fresh conscript levies, it was clear that the overall quality of the infantryman was going to drop. Not only was he going to be a poorer marksman, but his lack of training and battle experience were going to make him more nervous in combat. Quantity was going to have to replace quality in marksmanship as well as manpower, and a lot more ammunition was going to be needed if he was ever

Although it was possible for a trained professional to achieve high sustained rates of fire with a single-shot breech-loader, the repeater made it easier for the half-trained conscript. As repeating actions and rifle-calibre machine guns have become more and more effective, culminating in the very high rates of fire of 8,000 shots per minute achieved by modern electrically driven 'Vulcan' machine guns, it is clear that the ratio of rounds per casualty continues to

get worse. In World War I, the Americans expended 7,000 rounds of rifle-calibre ammunition per casualty; in World War II, 25,000; in Korea, 50,000, and for Vietnam the estimates range between 200,000 and 400,000. These figures also of course reflect the greatly increased difficulty of hitting mechanized or airborne targets.

In muzzle-loading days there were certainly attempts to produce repeaters. The obvious method was to increase the number of barrels, usually to two, either to ease the problem of reloading on horseback, as with the British Jacob's cavalry carbine, or for specialist issue to maintain parity with a known foe, as with the double-barrelled weapons issued to Corsican Gendarmes and Voltigeurs to give them a fighting chance against the local bandits who favoured double-barrelled shotguns. This approach was not popular with the infantry, since the soldier had to bear the entire weight of his weapon.

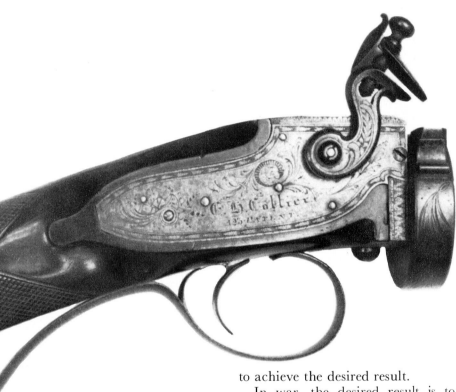

to achieve the desired result.

In war, the desired result is to immobilize the enemy and dissuade or prevent him from firing back, thus gaining for oneself a tactical advantage. This can be attained not only by wounding or killing him, but also by 'keeping his head down' through a continuous and concentrated barrage of fire which, in small-arms terms, reaches its maximum efficiency with the machine gun, but can be approached in volume though not actual effectiveness by the very large-scale use of extremely rapid rifle fire.

Lightness could of course be achieved by dispensing with the additional barrels and adopting a single barrel combined with a revolving cylinder containing several loaded chambers. The American Elisha Collier had designed a successful flintlock revolver, and later he adapted his system to percussion ignition. He demonstrated the latter version before a Select Committee of the British Ordnance Board in 1824, achieving a

rate of fire of 100 rounds in 29 minutes, hardly a significant improvement over a regulation musket. This demonstrated the fundamental drawback of any repeater using loose powder and ball. Sustained fire was precluded by the slow rate of reloading.

Colt produced a series of revolving percussion rifles based on the designs of his Chief Engineer, Elisha King Root. The .56-calibre (14.2-mm), five-shot rifles had a ballistic performance approaching that of the .58 (14.73-mm) American regulation musket of the Civil War; they were mass produced, and, in Colt's view, were ideal light-infantry weapons. The function of light infantry was to act as a 'screen', clearing the way for and protecting the advance of the main body of infantry. They were expected to manoeuvre 'with the greatest promptitude', so the problem of recharging a muzzle-loader whilst on the move was particularly acute, and a five-shooter offered a real advantage.

The revolver rifle never achieved much popularity, and the reasons are not hard to find. Hot gas and flame inevitably escaped between cylinder and barrel, burned the shooter's left arm if he held the rifle in the conventional way, and were distressingly close to the face. Worse, if there was an accidental 'flash over' between chambers, causing an accidental multiple discharge, the left arm was in the line of fire.

To be successful, a repeating rifle required self-contained cartridges and some form of magazine other than a revolving cylinder. The first effective magazine appeared as early as 1848 in the form of a tube running underneath the rifle barrel and containing cartridges 'nose to tail', pushed back towards the breech mechanism by spring pressure. This was the brainchild of the American

Some early repeating weapons used the system of superimposed loads. Several charges, each separated from the others, were fired in sequence. This rifle, made by W. Mills of London c 1825, used a sliding percussion lock to fire each charge in turn.

Detail of cylinder and hammer of a Colt percussion revolving rifle. The rear leaf sight is in the raised position. None of this type of longarm was ever really satisfactory.

Walter Hunt, but it proved a failure, largely because of the unsatisfactory nature of the cartridge, which he described as 'a hollow cone of lead filled with powder, and the end covered with a thin piece of cork'. This valiant attempt at a caseless cartridge did not work very well, but the idea was developed very slowly through a number of improvements named after the perpetrating individual or company, hence the Jennings, the Smith and Wesson, the Volcanic and the New Haven Arms Co. None was a commercial success, and in 1857 one of the smaller stockholders of the New Haven Arms Co., Oliver Fisher Winchester, a prosperous shirt manufacturer, acquired title to the business.

Knowing little of firearms, Winchester employed Benjamin Tyler Henry, a master machinist who had worked at the Government Armoury at Springfield, Massachusetts, and for the mass-production gunmakers Robbins and Lawrence. In redesigning the Volcanic, Henry incorporated a rather vulgar brass-framed action that was cheap to make and finish, and improved the lever-action repeating mechanism. As we have seen, Smith and Wesson were at one

American Volcanic carbine of .36 (9-mm) calibre with a 14-in (35.5-cm) barrel. The magazine tube is sited below the barrel, and the 'rocket-ball' projectiles are pushed back towards the loading mechanism by a spring-loaded 'follower', the finger-piece for which is seen in the curve at the lower front of the receiver. By pushing this piece towards the muzzle as far as it will go, and then rotating the forward section of the magazine to the side, the mouth of the magazine is exposed for charging.

Henry .44 rim-fire rifle. Its Volcanic parentage is obvious: the loading sequence is the same, but the fragile, low-powered 'rocket ball' has been replaced by a sturdier, more powerful .44 (11.2-mm) rim-fire cartridge.

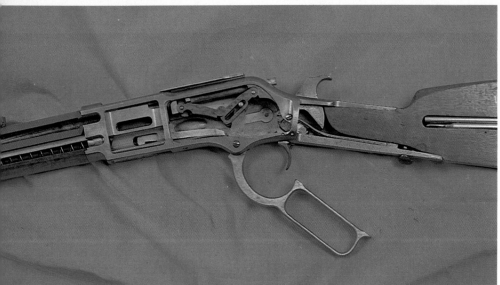

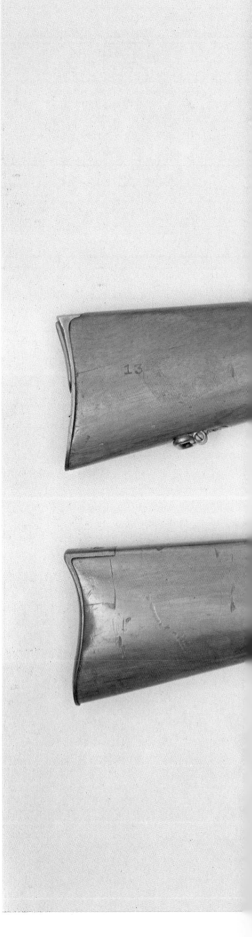

Top and above
Two views of the American
Winchester 1876 cutaway action.
The photographs show the toggle
lock holding the breech shut, and
being straightened into the locking
position as the lever is pulled back.
Imperial War Museum, London.

Right
Top. The Spencer repeater. Its
strong construction makes a
notable contrast with the elegant
but fragile Henry.
Bottom. Colt revolving rifle. The
problem of the leakage of hot gas
and flame between barrel and
cylinder could only be overcome by
means of a reciprocating cylinder
capable of moving forward to
enclose the rear of the barrel,
creating a gas seal. This added
greatly to mechanical complexity
and expense, and was not adopted
by Colt, who favoured simplicity
and economical volume production.

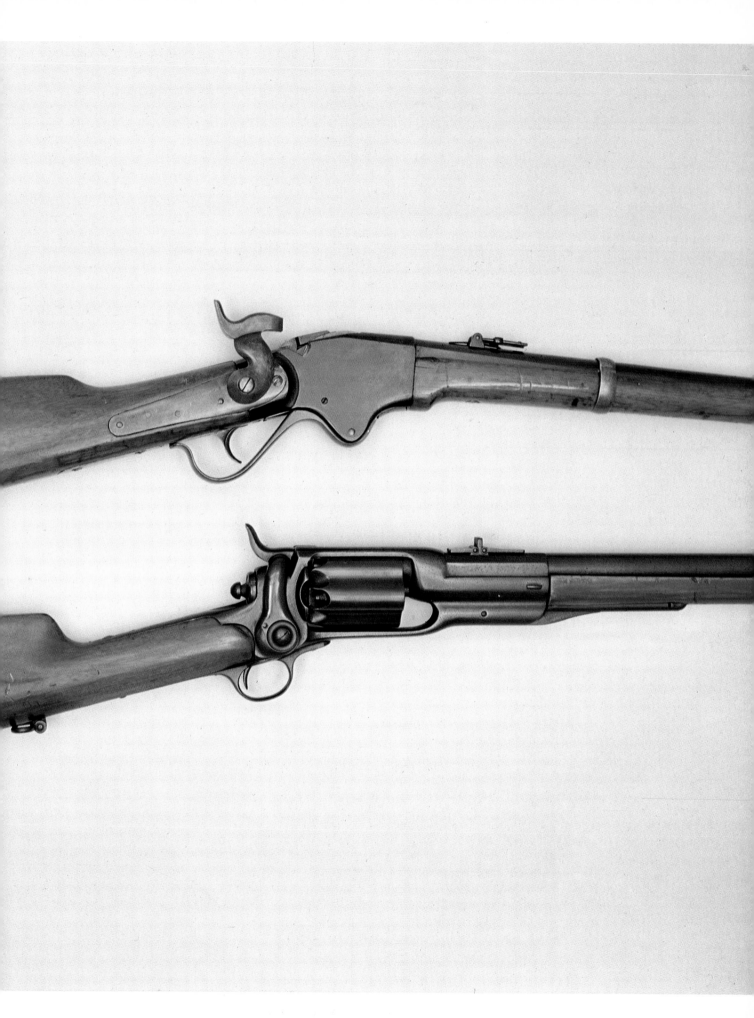

time involved with the weapon, and certain parallel rights to their patents were owned by Winchester, including the right to use the base-fire metallic cartridge patented by them in 1854. This was the first truly effective self-contained metallic cartridge, produced by them in a tiny .22 (5.6-mm) size still in service today in shooting galleries.

Henry doubled the calibre to .44 (11.2 mm) and backed it with a hefty charge of 28 grains of black powder. By today's standards this is merely a medium-power pistol cartridge, but it was a reasonable man-stopper, at any rate up to 200 yd (183 m). The Henry rifle did hold 16 rounds, and an experienced operator could fire two shots a second. Around 10,000 Henry rifles were used during the American Civil War (1861–65), and it was one of the only two repeaters in widespread issue. While it was quite well liked, its magazine was slow to load, delicate, prone to denting, and not fully enclosed. Dirt and foreign matter could thus easily foul the mechanism. In 1866 the weapon was substantially improved by incorporating a loading gate in the action and enclosing the magazine. The rifle was then renamed the Winchester and became the first of a series of successful civilian sporting arms of that name.

The Henry rifle was far outclassed, however, by another Civil War repeater, designed by Christopher Milne Spencer. Operated by an underlever like the Henry, the Spencer's breech rolled back through an arc and picked up a cartridge from a tubular seven-shot magazine protectively housed in the butt, then rolled back again to chamber it. The hammer had to be cocked separately. Although the Spencer was not capable of quite such rapid fire as the Henry, it was in every other way a greatly superior military rifle. It fired a .56-in (14.2-mm) calibre rim-fire cartridge which, although inferior to the muzzle-loading .58 (14.7-mm) Springfield in long-range performance, was far more effective than the Henry. The Spencer and the Henry each cost $40, exactly twice the price of a muzzle-loading musket complete with bayonet. The United States Government acquired 94,196 Spencer cavalry carbines and 13,171 rifles.

The Spencer had its effect on tactics. Union officers perfected the technique of ordering a single volley and then pausing. The opposing troops, assuming that the Northerners were laboriously recharging muzzle-loaders, would then break cover, to be slaughtered by a storm of bullets as the remaining six rounds in each magazine were discharged in about eight seconds. General Custer instructed his dismounted Michigan cavalrymen, who were fighting as infantry, to deliver a continuous fire while on the move, rather than pausing to shoot. While this barrage may not have been accurate, it did perform the entirely justifiable function of keeping the enemy's heads down, forcing them to retreat and stopping them from shooting back.

One other development of outstanding military importance is associated with the Spencer, although it was not utilized as fully as it should have been. With the Spencer, the problem of sustaining fire was substantially eliminated by means of the Blakeslee cartridge box. This box looked like an archer's quiver, and contained 10 tubes, each holding seven cartridges. When the Spencer was empty, a fresh tubeful of cartridges could instantly be pushed into the rifle's butt, and the riflemen could fire 77 rounds with only the briefest pauses for reloading, during which a round could be left ready in the chamber.

The Spencer had one drawback which, in military eyes, damned it. Its stubby little cartridge provided a high rainbow-like trajectory which made it effective only at short or point-blank ranges. In the black-powder era, the only way to improve ballistic performance was to increase the powder charge, which required a bigger, longer cartridge case. The Spencer design, with its breech-block swinging through an arc, could not be efficiently adapted for long cartridges.

By the end of the Civil War, the armies of the world were convinced that some sort of breech-loader was a necessity, but were faced with the choice either of a rather low-powered repeater or a long-range single-shot weapon. For reasons explained in the previous chapter, nearly all opted for a powerful single-shot type. The Turks nevertheless appreciated the advantages of firepower at close range, and purchased 30,000 Spencers and 30,000 Winchester Model 1866 .44 (11.2-mm) rim-fire rifles, ostensibly for cavalry use.

The first nation seriously to attempt the general issue of a repeater was Switzerland, whose Federal Parliament decreed re-arming with a Vetterli repeater in 1869. This rifle used a copper-cased rim-fire cartridge, and the large and clumsy but otherwise adequate Vetterli bolt action combined with a Winchester-style tubular magazine under the barrel.

The usefulness of the repeater was emphasized by several engagements during the Russo-Turkish War (1877–78). The Turks in defence at Plevna in 1877 had issued almost every soldier with both a Peabody-Martini single-shot and a Winchester .44 (11.2-mm) lever-action rim-fire. On two separate occasions this combination of long-range accuracy and short-range firepower stopped Russian frontal assaults with terrible loss of life. In two attacks, the Russian General Todleben lost 30,000 men.

With the Model 1876, Winchester had at last produced a lever-action in a calibre worthy of serious military consideration, the .45/75, firing a 350-grain bullet backed by 75 grains of black powder, a marginally more effective specification than the contemporary US .45/70 Government round. The '76 action was really only a strengthened version of the '66 and '73 toggle locks, but it was adequate. Besides sporting versions, a military rifle and a military carbine were offered, both with almost full-length forestocks completely concealing and thus protecting the tubular magazine. This was about the only repeater remotely suitable for military issue that was commercially available in quantity in the mid-1870s, yet it achieved few sales. The Turks and the Royal Canadian Mounted Police bought a handful, but the weapon made no direct mili-

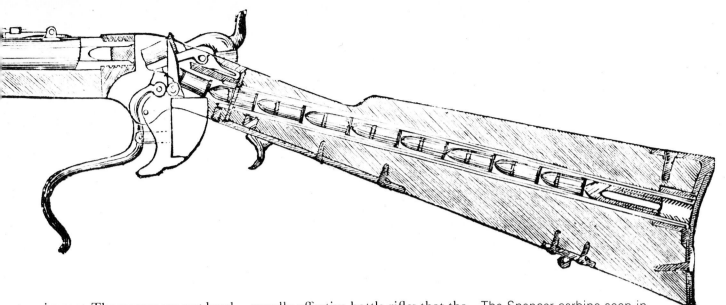

tary impact. The reasons are not hard to find: the Winchester toggle-lock action was considered too complex and fragile by many European experts, and the lever action interfered with bayonet fighting. More importantly, the major industrial powers wished to make military arms in their own factories rather than be dependent on a commercial concern in another state thousands of miles away. Poorer nations wanted something cheap and simple, either obsolescent surplus rifles or a basic-economy arm such as the Remington Rolling Block. The Turks, on the other hand, were unindustrialized, but they had a constant and active Russian threat on their borders, and so could not afford to economize on military hardware.

The Prussians had friendly relations with the Turks, and observed with interest their conflict with the Russians. They were also aware that their own signal success in overcoming the French in 1870 had been achieved despite their Needle Gun, not because of it. Their overwhelming victory had made them the arbiters of military fashion in Europe, and most of their potential enemies were displaying an alarmingly sincere form of flattery by attempting to bring their own armies up to Prussian standards of efficiency. Next time the going was not likely to be nearly so easy, and the French were already showing signs of wanting to resume hostilities.

The Prussian Model 71 single-shot was a fine rifle, but it had no significant tactical superiority over the

equally effective battle rifles that the other European powers had hastened to adopt. So far as the Prussians could see, there was only one alternative, a repeater. The Winchester-style magazine worked well, and the French Navy had begun to adopt a sort of tubular-magazine repeating Gras, the Kropatschek, as early as 1878. This modification was the brainchild of an Austrian, von Kropatschek, later the director of the Austrian state arsenal. The Prussians adopted a tubular magazine system in 1884, based on their Model 71, and christened it the 71/84.

While it was possible to convert the 71, all Model 71/84 weapons were a new production, and Mauser took the opportunity of adding minor mechanical improvements, including a better trigger action. They were supplied to units along the French frontier, where they came to the notice of their unfriendly neighbours in 1885. Consternation followed, French war fever cooled somewhat, and the Germans could congratulate themselves on being a good step ahead, equipped with a superb repeating rifle of proven performance and excellent reliability.

Needless to say, most first-class powers had not been entirely idle where repeaters were concerned. The Russians equipped some of their rifles with 'quick loaders', simple containers screwed to the side of the rifle and holding a few cartridges so that the loading hand had only to move a few inches to seize a fresh round instead of having to scrabble in a cartridge pouch or along a

The Spencer carbine seen in section. The drawing demonstrates how difficult it would be to design such a 'swinging-arc' repeating mechanism for any but cartridges of short overall length. Any increase in cartridge length must add not only to the overall length of the action, but to its depth.

bandoleer. These proved a palliative but not a cure. As we have already seen, it was becoming increasingly clear that there was only one logical choice for a military repeater, and that was some form of bolt-action.

The British and the Americans had evinced interest in the bolt-action repeater of James Paris Lee. His 1879 patent was for a 'bolt action' fitted with a box magazine beneath the receiver, in which five cartridges were carried one on top of the other, a radical departure from the 'nose-to-tail' arrangement of the Winchester tubular magazine. The box magazine was not actually invented by Lee, since there exists an English 1867 patent by Walker, Money and Little, but he certainly deserves the credit for its popularization.

The 1879 Lee was purchased in small numbers by the US Navy to test alongside the Hotchkiss, with a magazine in the butt, and the Remington Keene which had a tubular magazine beneath the barrel. Spain, Argentina and China also bought the Model 1879. In 1879, a Small Arms Committee was formed in England to deliberate, among other matters, on the desirability of adopting a magazine rifle. In 1880 the Lee was tested alongside the

Above
Russian Moisin-Nagant Model 1891 rifle. Despite a rather over-complicated bolt construction, these arms were well liked and strong. This example has the later 1908-pattern rear-sight for use with the higher-velocity light round.

Above left
French Lebel rifle of 1886. This close-up of the action of the first high-velocity small-bore military repeater shows the cartridge carrier which tipped downwards to receive a cartridge from the magazine running below the barrel; it then raised the round into position to be pushed forward into the chamber by the bolt. Imperial War Museum, London.

Left
Austrian Model 1888 Mannlicher straight-pull action. This clip-loaded 8-mm rifle was originally made for an 8-mm black-powder load, which was superseded by a more powerful smokeless version in 1890. Although very well made, this Model 1888 action used a weak wedge lock that was unsuitable for high-pressure smokeless loads. A much stronger action with a rotating bolt-head was adopted in 1890 for cavalry and in 1895 for infantry. Imperial War Museum, London.

Right
Krag Jorgensen bolt-action rifle. This Norwegian design was highly regarded because of its very smooth bolt action. Its unusual magazine, mounted on the right side, is shown open, ready to receive cartridges. Imperial War Museum, London.

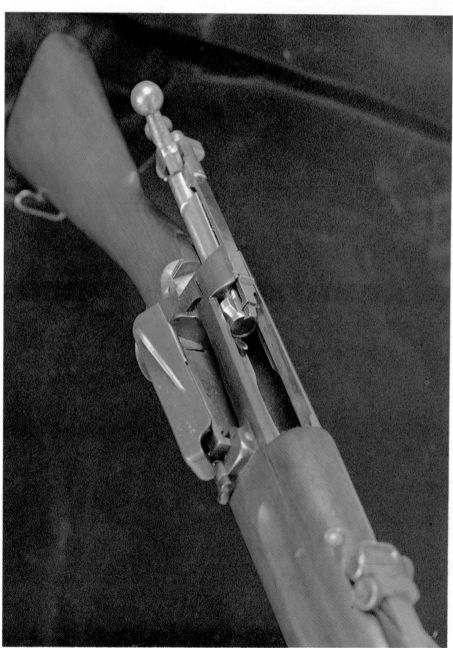

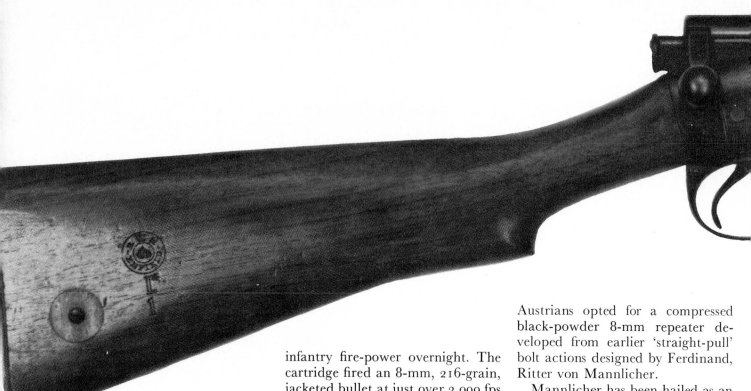

The Lee-Metford rifle, Great Britain's first general-issue bolt-action repeating army rifle. Its two-piece stock and large capacity but relatively unprotected magazine provoked criticism from professional gunmakers, but caused few problems in service.

Hotchkiss, Kropatschek, Winchester 1876, Gardner Green and Vetterli. The Lee's bolt action was criticized, but its magazine and its (hotly disputed) ease of manufacture were well liked. Over the next four years nearly 50 magazine rifles or quick-loading systems were examined by the Committee, but only three were not rejected: the Improved Lee, the Improved Lee with Bethel Burton magazine, and the Owen Jones. This last was equipped with a form of slide action, not a bolt, and was considered superior to the Lee, but was dropped because of potential manufacturing difficulty and cost.

In 1886, the French Army introduced the 8-mm Lebel. The rifle was nothing remarkable, little more than a strengthened Gras/Kropatschek retaining the tubular magazine. Its cartridge, however, was a sensation, revolutionizing the effectiveness of infantry fire-power overnight. The cartridge fired an 8-mm, 216-grain, jacketed bullet at just over 2,000 fps (609 mps). These extraordinary ballistics were achieved with a new and somewhat unstable propellant, a nitrocellulose compound called 'Poudre B'.

This new powder was smokeless, but while the banishment of enveloping clouds of smoke from the field of Mars was a worthwhile side effect, the real reason for the development of this new powder was to achieve a greatly improved ballistic efficiency. The very flat trajectory of the new Lebel cartridge produced a greatly increased 'danger zone', making precise range estimation a less crucial aspect of securing a battlefield hit. The high-velocity, hard-jacketed bullet also had much greater penetration than the old low-velocity soft bullet. The Lebel would punch through brick walls or stout trees that hitherto had provided safe cover, and would bring with it an accompanying shower of hazardous splinters. The battlefield had again become a much more perilous place.

Germany decided to copy 'Poudre B' and set up a commission to design a new rifle. Britain finally agreed on the Lee bolt-action and magazine, with a Metford barrel designed to minimize fouling and a .303 (7.69-mm) cartridge based on Swiss developments, propelled by a compressed charge of black powder. The Austrians opted for a compressed black-powder 8-mm repeater developed from earlier 'straight-pull' bolt actions designed by Ferdinand, Ritter von Mannlicher.

Mannlicher has been hailed as an arms inventor of genius, and his contributions to metallurgy and early automatic designs are not in doubt, but the practicability of many of his earlier patents is open to question, and his two main influences on the arms technology of the 1880s, the straight-pull bolt and the Mannlicher clip, are not without their drawbacks in military service. Most bolt actions are 'turn-bolts', and the bolt handle must be lifted up to unlock the mechanism before the bolt is pulled back. Properly designed, the lifting of the handle does in fact begin to withdraw the bolt and exerts a very strong camming action to withdraw a fired cartridge case which might (if all has not gone well) be sticking in the chamber. Similarly, when the bolt is closed, the camming action will seat a reluctant round. Mannlicher reasoned that a 'straight pull', where the shooter did not first have to lift the handle, but merely jerked it straight back, would make for greater rapidity of fire. In return for a very marginal gain in speed, he sacrificed powerful primary extraction. Later straight-pull military designs, the American Lee Navy rifle and the notorious Canadian Ross, which frequently jammed in the mud of World War I trenches, also suffered from this problem. Only the Swiss Schmidt-Rubin, which used very

different mechanical principles, managed to overcome the weakness and practical unhandiness of the straight-pull design.

Mannlicher's clip of 1885 was a metal packet holding five (or thereabouts) cartridges. The entire packet was loaded into a single box-type magazine, and, after the final round was fired, the empty clip dropped out of the bottom of the magazine. This is clearly a much quicker and more fumble-free method of reloading than having to grope for and insert cartridges one by one. Its disadvantages are the impossibility of 'topping up' a partly empty magazine, the weight and expense of the clip and, most important of all, the hole that must be left in the bottom of the magazine which, although allowing the egress of the exhausted clip, also admits foreign matter.

This clip was manifestly an improvement on the tubular magazine which not only had to be single-loaded, but with centre-fire cartridges was inherently dangerous, since, except in the Lebel version, the nose of the bullet rested on the primer of the cartridge in front. Sharp recoil combined with the inertia of the cartridges could cause a cartridge to explode.

The Mannlicher clip was adopted by the German Commission for their Model 88 rifle, along with a modification of the Model 71 bolt. The Model '88 action, incidentally, was also produced at the Steyr factory in Austria, and, slightly modified, took on the 'Mannlicher' name and be-

came the basis of the Italian Model 91 Mannlicher-Carcano, Rumanian Model 93, Dutch Model 95 and Greek Model 1903 service rifles. Without doubt, the German Commission achieved a signal success with their selection of cartridge, a 7.9-mm type firing a 227-grain, round-nosed bullet at 2,034 fps (620 mps), which, with occasional improvements, served as the standard German service cartridge until after World War II. This cartridge was also 'rimless', the protruding rim being replaced by a groove or cannelure for engagement by the extractor. This made for easier feeding through the magazine.

In 1889, with his Belgian rifle, Mauser improved on the Mannlicher clip. Mauser introduced a simple, expendable five-round charger that gripped the cartridges by their extraction cannelures. The magazine was filled by inserting either end of the clip into guideways on the receiver. Thumb pressure stripped the rounds into the magazine. Pushing the bolt forward to chamber the first round automatically ejected the clip. An altogether lighter, neater system, it permitted 'topping up' of the magazine. To build the Model 89, the famous Fabrique Nationale d' Armes de Guerre (FN) was set up in Belgium, with 50% German ownership; but the rifle was also made in Liège and, during World War I, by Hopkins and Allen in America and the État Belge factory, staffed by refugees, in Birmingham.

By 1892, all the Great Powers

were armed or arming with small-bore bolt-action magazine rifles, the Japanese converting their Murata rifles to 8-mm in 1889 and the Russians having adopted the 7.62-mm Moisin-Nagant, a synthesis of Russian and Belgian designs, in 1891. America was now running last, having clung since 1873 to her Allin-actioned 45/70 Springfields for Army issue. In 1892, the USA adopted the Krag Jorgensen, designed by the Director and Chief Armourer of the Norwegian Kongsberg arms factory. The Krag was a 'rifleman's rifle', with a slick, smooth, easily manipulated bolt action. It also was equipped with a peculiar magazine, on the right-hand side, that could be recharged with the bolt forward and the rifle loaded. Flicking the loading gate open eased the magazine spring tension, and rounds could very quickly be dropped in, without careful positioning. The US version of the action was unnecessarily weak, however, since the second locking lug of the Norwegian rifle was omitted, and the design was expensive to manufacture. The round chosen by America was the .30/40, a rimmed cartridge ballistically similar to the British .303 (7.69-mm).

Thus by the early 1890s, all nations with any pretensions to being world powers were similarly armed (Great Britain having adopted Cordite smokeless powder in 1892). Although all had well made and at least adequate and safe military weapons, without exception they had drawbacks. The German 88 Commission

American Lee Navy Model 1895 rifle. Although referred to as a 'straight pull', the bolt handle does move through a 25° arc to unlock the action. The high-velocity 6-mm rifle suffered from severe bore erosion with the powders of the day, and the rifle was not well liked. Pattern Room, Royal Small Arms Factory, Enfield.

rifle had a fragile extractor and was capable of firing without the front section of the bolt in place, with potentially disastrous results. The Lee-Metford's barrel very rapidly wore out with Cordite loads, and had to be replaced with an Enfield design. To make matters worse, most second-line powers followed Belgium's lead and began to rearm themselves with an ever-improving series of Mauser-designed clip-loading rifles. These were by and large commercial designs with only minor

cosmetic variations to suit the whims of different clients.

After severe military maulings, both America and Britain became true believers in the Mauser credo. During the Spanish American War in 1898, American Regulars had Krags, and State Militias .45/70 Springfields. At San Juan Hill, 15,000 American troops, with insurgent support, eventually overran 700 Mauser-armed Spaniards, but only after incurring 1,400 casualties. It is likely that this level of loss would have been far exceeded had intelligent use not been made of some Gatling machine guns. Britain, chastened by the performance of the Boer irregulars, also turned her mind to the task of finding a military rifle of improved performance.

A period of Great Power reappraisal began. France started a somewhat haphazard partial reequipment with arms based on the Berthier action, the invention of an officer of the Algerian Railway Company. This singularly unlovely changeling was essentially a Lebel with most of the drawbacks removed. Most important of all, a three-shot Mannlicher clip replaced the tubular magazine. Why a three-cartridge capacity was chosen when those of most Continental armies held five, and the British version 10, can only be attributed to a desire to give the rifle a less pot-bellied appearance.

Such aesthetic considerations were abandoned during World War I, when many were converted to five-shot. Of greater international importance was France's introduction of a solid bronze pointed bullet, the 'Balle D', in 1898. The point decreased air resistance, made the round less susceptible to being blown off-course by side winds, and greatly increased its effective range. America, Britain and France were obsessed with very long-range performance, partly in response to the improved ballistics of various Mauser-pattern cartridges and partly to give the infantry at least some chance of making an effective reply to field artillery.

The Germans introduced a stronger, safer, Mauser bolt-action in 1898. They retained the 7.9-mm cartridge, although many experts favoured a smaller bore, because of the need to maintain standardization during the inevitably gradual replacement of the Model 88. The Mauser 98 was, at the time, generally if not universally accepted to have the finest military-rifle action in existence; it was strong, safe, with a very fast lock time and reasonably straightforward to manufacture. Before and after World War I, a 98-based rifle became almost the only reasonable choice for any nation choosing to rearm, and the action was made in Belgium, China, Mexico, Spain, Czechoslovakia, Poland, Yugoslavia, Japan and Austria as well as by the various German Government arsenals and a plethora of German commercial factories.

Having to deal with ungrateful colonial rebels as well as 'civilized' enemies, the British and the Americans had come to three conclusions:

they needed shorter, lighter, handier rifles that were more suitable for snap-shooting, they needed clip-loaders, preferably the fashionable Mauser, and they needed more powerful ammunition. Philippino Moros, Sudanese Dervishes and wily Pathans, if suitably fuelled with adrenalin, proved to be singularly unhindered by the little holes drilled by the relatively sedate .30/40 and .303 (7.69-mm) jacketed projectiles. Something on a par with the smashing power of the old .45 (11.4-mm) lead bullet seemed to be what was required, and Great Britain embarked on a long series of experiments with expanding bullets; amongst the most successful was the soft-point developed by Captain Bertie Clay of the Indian ammunition factory at Dum Dum. While this and other designs were reasonably efficient, they were banned for warfare between signatories of the First Hague Convention of 1899, and the problems of double-supply systems caused Britain to phase them out completely in 1905. The higher-velocity German Spitzer round produced a gratifying increase in stopping power by releasing its great energy very quickly, causing not a neat little hole but a large, temporary cavity that created substantial physical and nervous trauma.

The United States adopted the Springfield rifle in 1903, and a new rimless .30 (7.62-mm) cartridge based on German Spitzer designs in 1906. It had a 24-in (60.96-cm) barrel, and no carbine version was issued. Despite being called after the American national armoury, the Springfield rifle was essentially an unnecessarily over-complicated American modification of the 98

Most military rifles made provision for the attachment of a bayonet to convert it into a stabbing weapon.
From top to bottom
French Lebel bayonet M1886/93/16 with all-metal scabbard.
German Mauser 98/05 pattern bayonet with steel scabbard adopted in 1915.
Bayonet for the British Lee Enfield rifle P.1907.

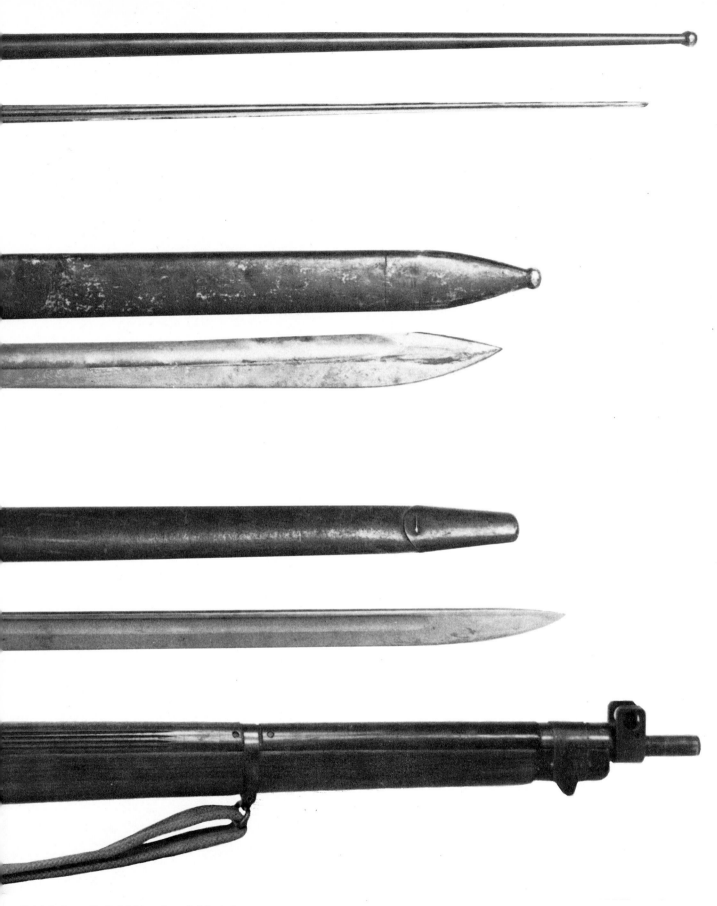

British Lee-Enfield Number 4 Mark I
rifle. This arm was intended to be
easier to produce than the old
SMLE, but also had better sights
and was inherently more accurate.

Mauser action, for which the US Government paid Mauser $200,000.

In England, improvements were gradual. In 1902, it was decided to substitute a Swiss-style general-issue short rifle to replace various infantry, artillery and cavalry pattern arms, and in 1905 to introduce charger-loading, with two five-round clips being used to load the 10-round magazines. The result was the Short Magazine Lee-Enfield Mark III of 1907, which in conjunction with the more lethal Spitzer-type Mark VII high-velocity .303 (7.69-mm) round issued in 1910, made a most reliable service rifle in the two world wars.

The lure of the Mauser still affected Britain, however, and a high-velocity .276 (7-mm) Mauser-actioned five-shot rifle known as the Pattern 13 was given limited issue for troop trials in 1913. It can be argued that this high-performance cartridge gave too much recoil even for season-ed regulars to handle, but, with minor reservations about extractor strength, the British version of the Mauser action was excellent. The outbreak of war made the introduction of a new cartridge unwise, but, modified slightly to accept .303 (7.69-mm) rounds, the Enfield went into quantity production as the Pattern 14 in three American factories. On a basis of individual examples these were fine rifles, but America could not meet British standards of interchangeability of parts, and the Eddystone factory's heat treatment was uncertain and dangerous. As sufficient Lee-Enfields became available, production of the Pattern 14 was phased out. On America's entry into the war in 1917, production was resumed on a .30/06 version, called the P.17, and these soon outnumbered Springfields in service with the United States.

World War I is more fully discussed in the chapter devoted to automatic weapons, but the effect of the war on rifle design is also of some importance. It emerged that a single pattern of short rifle was more economical and efficient than a plethora of clumsy long rifles and handy but ballistically inefficient and hard-kicking carbines. Germany in due course adopted a short rifle,

Below
British SMLE .303 rifle. This example had a chequered career. After capture from the Turks, it fell into the hands of King Faisal I, and he presented it to Colonel T. E. Lawrence, whose initials may be seen just above the magazine. After using it with some success against the Turks, Lawrence presented it to King George V. It is now on display in the Imperial War Museum, London.

Right
World War I was fought with the majority of infantry on both sides armed with bolt-action magazine rifles. Here British and Australian troops are shown entering a ruined village, carrying the Short Magazine Lee-Enfield rifle.

Below
A Russian guerilla encampment in the Uvarovo District near Moscow. The partisan in the foreground is carrying a Model 1891/30 rifle. Also in evidence are a PPSh sub-machinegun and a dismounted DT tank machinegun.

the Kar 98k, and most other nations that rearmed in the inter-war period chose a variant of this arm. Britain continued her search for a new rifle, but achieved only the No. 4, a Lee-Enfield more suitable for economic mass production, more accurate, and with better sights. The French introduced an excellent, simple, easily made bolt-action for a 7.5 rimless round, the MAS M36 (Manufacture d'Armes de St Etienne, Modèle 1936), but few reached the hands of troops before the outbreak of war.

In truth, most nations realized their next rifle ought to be a semi-automatic, but could not contemplate the expense of replacing their huge stocks of well-made bolt-actions. Only America made any wide-scale issue of a semi-automatic, the M1 Garand adopted in 1936. World War II was fought using, often literally, the rifles of 1914–18.

Nor is the bolt action yet militarily dead. Quite apart from its use as a sniper weapon in Britain, America, France and Austria, all of whom have produced significant post-war advances in this specialist field, the older, more homely bolt-actions still serve throughout the forces of the Third World, if only for second-line troops. It will be many years yet before the Mausers and Lee-Enfields fire their last shots in anger.

American firepower somewhere in Belgium. A member of an armoured infantry regiment mortar squad, equipped with an M1 Garand; leaning against the wall is an M1 carbine.

Automatic Weapons

David Penn

With the increasing use of the repeating rifle during the last quarter of the nineteenth century, it was becoming ever more evident that, in certain conditions, infantry could lay down such a volume of sustained fire that they could neutralize an enemy by preventing him from moving or from shooting back. A clear advantage lay with the army in defence, assuming well-chosen ground,

bullet-proof concealment and a 'built-in' rifle rest. A feeling of protection and something to lean on does wonders for the combat efficiency of riflemen. Troops in attack, by contrast, tended to present themselves as fully exposed targets and were required to move quickly, often under full pack, while their hidden opponents might present only tiny targets to shoot at. Their standard of

Lewis gun in action with the 15th Royal Scots in January 1918. The bipod is not in use and the barrel jacket rests directly on the sandbag to maintain a low profile.

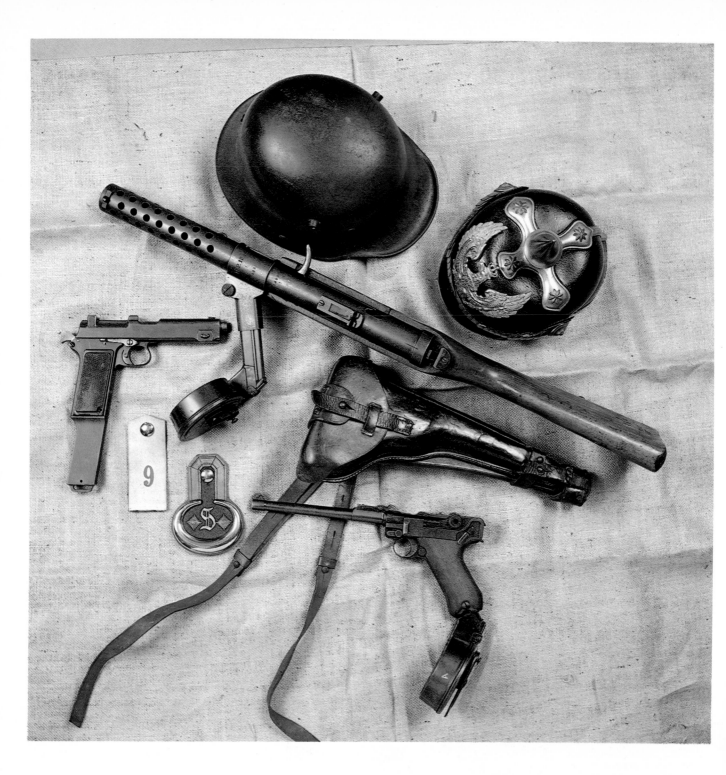

Evolution of the machine-pistol.
The lower weapon is the German
'Artillery' Parabellum pistol, fitted
with a 32-round 'Snail-drum'
magazine and accompanied by its
detachable shoulder stock/holster.
This arm was not capable of fully
automatic fire. Left, a very rare
Austrian Steyr 16-shot fully
automatic pistol. Top is the
Bergmann MP 18.1. This
submachine gun uses the same
barrel, covered by a perforated
jacket, and magazine as the
Artillery Parabellum. Imperial War
Museum, London.

marksmanship was inevitably much lower.

The greater effectiveness of the army in defence was widely agreed, but the function of an army and its generals is to overcome the enemy, and no general can expect to retain his command if he plans and trains only for defensive action. If he is to win, at some point he must advance, if only to re-possess national territory formerly occupied by the invader. In attack, therefore, it was necessary to accept losses in order to succeed.

By 1914, a new factor had established itself, one that gave an even greater advantage to the defence. This was the machine gun, the 'essence of infantry', by which one man, or a crew of two or three, was capable of equalling the sustained firepower of 40 highly trained riflemen armed with bolt-action repeat-

ing rifles, or 60-80 similarly armed but inexperienced conscripts. The belt-fed medium machine gun, in combination with sophisticated deep entrenchments that were almost artillery-proof, dominated the first three years of World War I. The medium machine gun, supported on a firm tripod base and capable of an almost indefinite output of 600 rounds per minute, was, round for round, far more effective than an equivalent volume of rifle fire.

By 1917, during Haig's offensive, front-line German trenches were manned largely by highly trained veteran machine gun crews, the riflemen being held back to mop up or counter-attack. On several occasions, defence of British positions was left entirely to machine guns, the infantry serving merely as bearers to transport ammunition and water for

the cooling systems, and to load belts. The rifle was no longer queen of battlefields. To attack entrenched machine guns was to court near-certain bloody failure. Lloyd George attributed to the machine gun nearly 75% of the casualties of World War I, and no-one has seriously challenged this figure.

Almost from the first military use of firearms, the advantages of a high concentration of fire were appreciated, and more or less successfully attained by grouping together a number of barrels for simultaneous discharge. These unwieldy devices, known as 'ribaudequins' or 'organ guns', were intended for defence of narrow places, or to stop a cavalry attack or to break up an infantry phalanx immediately prior to an attack by one's cavalry, a technique used at the Battle of Piccardina in

Patented in 1718 by James Puckle of London, this was an early example of a hand-operated, rapid-fire weapon. Each chamber was loaded with one charge and rotated by the handle. Department of the Environment, London.

1467 by the Venetian condottiere, Bartolommeo Colleoni. This concentration of fire could not be sustained, however, and the guns took an unconscionable time to reload, during which they were highly vulnerable.

At the end of the eighteenth century light, highly manoeuvrable field artillery pieces were developed to achieve concentrated fire. Designed for anti-personnel use with shot, canister or grape, they were used much like giant shotguns, and their effective deployment by Napoleon Bonaparte helped compensate for the poor quality of much French infantry. The introduction of the long-range rifle musket temporarily shifted the balance of effectiveness again, but by the Franco Prussian War (1870–71) rifled field artillery

capable of far outranging any small arm had been introduced on a wide scale.

By 1870 the technological advances that had enabled the development of the metallic-cartridge repeating rifle had also made possible the design of sustained rapid-fire rifle-calibre weapons. Modern automatic weapons employ surplus energy from the firing cartridge to cycle the unloading and reloading mechanisms. Nevertheless, the first generation of 'machine guns' derived their motive power not from the pressure of expanding gas but from the stout right arm of the shooter operating either a rotating crank or a reciprocating handle.

The first such arm to make any military impact was a 50-barrelled piece demonstrated in Belgium by a

Right
Hiram Maxim with a highly engraved and lacquered Maxim gun, one of two presented to the Turks. Surprisingly, the usually perspicacious Turks showed little interest at first. One of these magnificent guns is now in the Imperial War Museum. Picture courtesy Lt-Col Maxim Joubert.

Below
Model 1871 Gatling on an all-metal Broadwell carriage. This example is believed to be one of the three prototype Model 1871s tested by the British Government in August and September 1870. The Gatling's superior effectiveness as an anti-personnel weapon over light field artillery and the French Mitrailleuse was proved and it was adopted by the Army and Navy. Imperial War Museum, London.

Captain Fafschamps in 1857, which generated mild interest among the armies of Europe. During the early days of the American Civil War, when the Union was in danger of being trounced, the Northern press howled for a wonder weapon with which to compensate for their lack of military ability. The cry for 'a Confederate-States-Milling-Machine which will go through . . . this war as if it were a bushel of wheat' fell fruitfully upon the ears of a successful designer of agricultural machinery, Richard Jordan Gatling. The son of a North Carolina plantation owner, Gatling duly applied himself to the design of a machine gun to 'enable one man to do as much battle duty as one hundred' so that 'exposure to battle and disease be greatly diminished'. Gatling marketed his gun patented in 1862 as a labour-saving device, pointing out that the rifle was labour-intensive and stressing the economic benefits of his weapon, since it cost a mere $1,500 in comparison with the equipment for a regiment, which amounted to $50,000. Despite vigorous marketing by the inventor, involving practical demonstrations on the battlefield, the Gatling, and another rather less efficient gun, the Ager, had no real military impact on the American Civil War. But Gatling persevered in improving his designs, which all involved several barrels, each with its own striker housed in a lock cylinder which rotated with the

barrels, and in 1866 he entered into a manufacturing agreement with the Colt company.

The first significant military use of machine guns occurred in the Franco-Prussian War in 1870. France had adopted in 1869 in conditions of great secrecy the Montigny *mitrailleuse*, a modification of Fafschamps' design. *Mitrailleuse* means 'grapeshotter', reflecting its intended role against men and horse, which it was expected to fulfil with greater precision than artillery. This 37-barrelled carriage-mounted gun was reliable, produced a rate of fire of 444 rounds a minute, but weighed about two tons complete with accessories and 2,100 rounds of ammunition. In order to preserve an element of surprise, the gun crews had been given no opportunity to practise or work out tactics on manoeuvres.

The Prussians had no machine guns, but had studied the Belgian version of the *mitrailleuse* and had assessed the Gatling in 1869 at Carlsbad, when one Gatling had scored 88% hits, as opposed to 27% by 100 riflemen with the same quantity of cartridges. It seems that they had given some thought to anti-machine gun tactics, since in an early engagement at Saarbrucken they deployed their troops in skirmishing lines, offering the worst possible target. The *mitrailleuse* nonetheless achieved some signal successes, giving belated credence to the ecstatic notices it was receiving in the Paris

press. At Montigny la Grange, aptly enough, and at Gravelotte the guns were placed in close support of infantry in defence, and the Germans made the error of attacking in close formation. In the latter battle von Moltke lost 13% of his men, considered a very high level in 'civilized' warfare.

There were thus three clear lessons learned from the Franco-Prussian War: the machine gun was highly lethal against massed, unprotected infantry; it operated most effectively in defence; it was large and unwieldy and thus highly vulnerable to artillery, which could outrange it.

A variety of very efficient hand-operated machine guns came on the market during the 1870s, including Gatlings which were capable of the astoundingly high rate of fire of 1,500 rounds per minute; the neat American Gardner, which was adopted for Royal Naval service in a two-barrelled tripod-mounted form, and the Swedish-designed, British-made Palmcranz Nordenfelt, also given Royal Naval issue. While none approached the monstrous weight of the *mitrailleuse*, all were multi-barrelled arms that for land service really required mounting on wheeled carriages. In varying degrees, they were unhandy and vulnerable. Nevertheless in suitably large calibres they enjoyed great naval popularity as anti-torpedo boat weapons, an ideal counter to a new threat. They also saw considerable colonial service, being effective enforcers of the 'Pax Brittanica' since few non-European armies possessed long-range artillery.

Although the feasibility of automatic arms operated by their own surplus energy had been demonstrated by E Lindner's 1856 patent for a gas-operated piston, by Spanish experiments in the 1860s, and by Karl Krnka's work in the early 1880s, the practical application of the concept can again be credited to an American, Hiram Maxim, already internationally known as a pioneer of gas and electric lighting. He opened up new horizons of potential carnage in 1883, at which time most nations had just about settled down with a reliable single-shot military

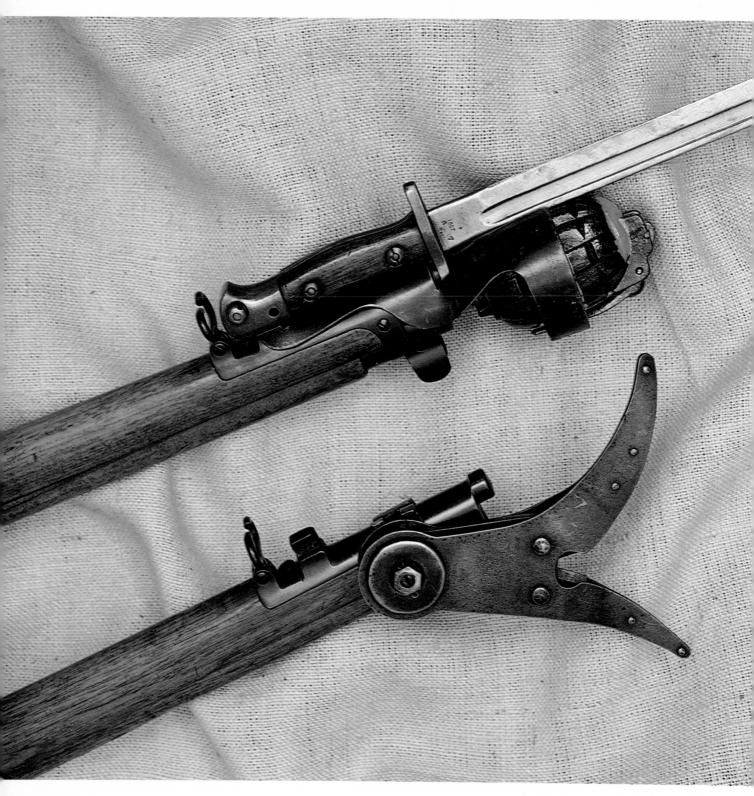

Weapons of the trench war, fitted to
the muzzles of Short Magazine Lee
Enfield rifles.
Top. Grenade discharger of 1916.
Bottom. Barbed wire cutters.
Pattern Room, Royal Small Arms
Factory, Enfield.

Browning-designed Colt Model 95 machine gun, the type used by US Marines in China during the 1900 Boxer Uprising.

rifle. Maxim devised a 'test bed' in his London workshop which allowed him to attach different arrangements of breech mechanisms and levers to his .45 Gardner Gatling calibre barrel, purchased from the highly sceptical manager of the Henry Rifle Barrel Co., who had predicted utter failure. Maxim, however, achieved complete success.

HRH the Duke of Cambridge, a powerful Royal military presence, and General Lord Wolseley were most impressed with Maxim's first effort, which boasted a hydraulic retarding system that allowed selection of a fully automatic rate of fire between 600 rounds and one round per minute. Convinced of the practicability of the machine gun, Maxim patented every system he could think of to achieve automatic fire, including recoil and gas operation, and went into partnership with Vickers Ltd, the shipbuilders, in 1884.

It is necessary to pause in the historical narrative and consider the three main methods of harnessing that part of the energy generated when a cartridge is fired that plays no part in the propulsion of the bullet. The surplus energy, which often amounts to 70% of the total produced, is largely wasted in heat, but two sources can be employed to produce automatic fire: recoil and gas pressure.

The simplest mechanism is called 'blowback'. The gas pressure that is pushing a fairly light bullet forwards out of the barrel is also attempting to push the fired cartridge case backwards out of the chamber. It is necessary to contain this rearward pressure to protect the shooter. In a simple blowback weapon the barrel remains rigidly in place, but the breech-bolt is capable of moving backwards, and is not mechanically locked in place while firing. The breech-block's mass is much greater than the bullet and it is also held forward under spring pressure. The great pressure developed by the firing cartridge does eventually overcome the inertia of the breech-block and drives it and the fired cartridge case backwards. At the end of its travel, having ejected the fired case along the way, the breech-block halts, and the compressed mainspring drives it forward. It picks up another round and chambers it, and the arm is ready to begin the firing cycle again. This system is simple and safe for low-pressure pistol cartridges, but is far less satisfactory for high-powered rifle cartridges operating at three times the pressure. It is nevertheless possible to incorporate a mechanical delay into the system to allow chamber pressure to drop to a safe level before the breech-block begins to move.

For high-pressure cartridges, the alternative is mechanically to lock breech-block and barrel together until pressure drops sufficiently. One way to achieve this is to allow both barrel and breech-block to recoil back, locked together, while the rest of the arm stays stationary. The rearward movement of the barrel ceases at a point when it and the breech-block are mechanically unlocked, and the latter continues rearwards to eject the fired case. If the barrel moves only a fraction of an inch before unlocking occurs, the system is termed 'short recoil'. Maxim's first machine gun used this principle. If the barrel moves a distance at least equal to the overall length of the cartridge, the method of operation is called 'long recoil'. This latter method results in a very slow mechanical cycle, and so receives little use.

The third system does not use the fired cartridge case as a piston, but utilizes the expanding gas to drive backwards a piston mounted alongside the barrel and connected to the locked breech-block. The gas to drive the piston is either captured at the muzzle or is bled off through a small port drilled in the wall of the barrel. Gas operation is deservedly very popular since gas flow may be regulated by adjusting the gas port, so variations in ammunition may be accommodated and the effects of fouling or dirt overcome. This system was first successfully employed by John Moses Browning, the most prolific and consistently successful gun designer of all time, although most of his work was on civilian arms and automatic pistols, and thus outside the scope of these chapters.

Hiram Maxim's short-recoil gun impressed the British Government, who in 1891 authorized an issue of two Maxims per Regular battalion. Volunteer battalions had to buy their own. Despite the underhand tactics of competitors, Maxim proved to the nations of Europe that his gun could out-perform all others in reliability and speed. Kaiser Wilhelm II, who had been converted to machine guns during a visit to England, and whose troops had been given their first lessons in machine-gun handling by British 10th Hussars instructors, witnessed the Maxim trials and stated, 'This is the gun. There is no other.' Despite Army indifference, eventually overcome by the 1901 trials, he pressed for its widespread issue and the development of proper tactics. The Russians were equally enthusiastic, and both nations eventually put versions into production in their own countries.

By 1903, 19 out of 28 armies using machine guns favoured Maxims, and 21 out of 24 navies. The Maxim in various modifications was the primary medium machine gun of Britain (where it was known as the Vickers), Germany (as the Maxim '08) and Russia during World War I.

Where Maxim trod, others followed. The Franco-Anglo-American firm of Hotchkiss, with the American Lawrence V. Benét as Chief Engineer, achieved some success with a gas-operated design based on the patents of an Austrian, Captain Baron Adolf von Odkolek. The air-cooled Model 1897 worked well enough, although it overheated and was fed by a 24 or 30-shot metal strip magazine that was very difficult to insert into the gun. This and later variants saw adoption by France, the United States, Japan, Brazil, Mexico, Spain and much of the Balkans. Browning's air-cooled, gas-operated 1895 model, made by Colt, was adopted by the US Navy and Mar-

ines, Spain, Italy and by some South American countries. It had a notably smooth and gentle action, but tended to overheat and 'cook off' a live round left in the chamber after prolonged firing.

No medium machine gun to match the Maxim's overall efficiency appeared until the introduction of the Browning Model 1917. This superb weapon was based on his 1900 patent, operated on the short-recoil principle, was exceptionally well thought-out, simple to use and trouble-free, and was designed for easy manufacture. In tests before Congress and the Press in February 1917, two guns fired 68,920 rounds without any hitch or failure. The United States, in possession of a hodge-podge of 1,100 obsolete machine guns, immediately ordered 45,000. By the time the Armistice was signed in November 1918 only a few had reached France, but the gun, in water-cooled and air-cooled forms, had a long and honourable service

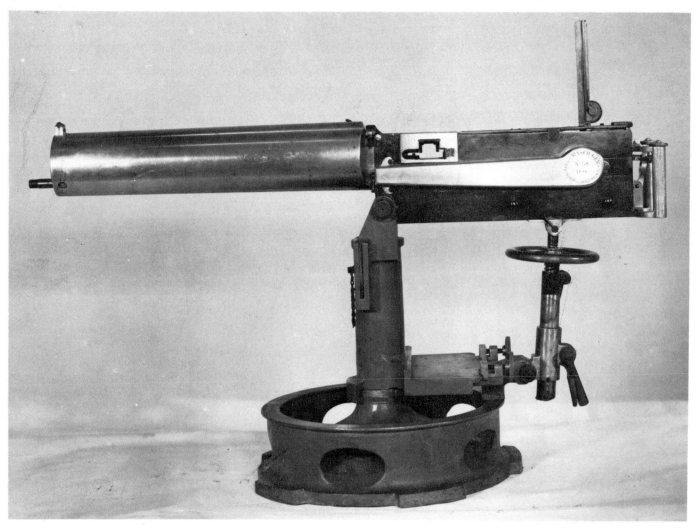

Above
German Maxim '08 on a tripod. This
gun replaced the expensive, heavy
and shiny brass water jacket of its
predecessor with more economical,
thinner steel. The main improvement
is in the sophisticated tripod mount,
which is capable of a wide range of
adjustment for high or low
positions on flat or irregular ground.

Right
The old but reliable, water-cooled
Vickers gun in action in North Africa
during World War II with men of the
Middlesex Regiment.

Left
A very early German Maxim. This
example, dated 1896, is essentially
identical to the contemporary
British Maxim. Despite the Kaiser's
enthusiasm, the value of the
machine gun was not generally
appreciated in the German Army
until after the turn of the century.

Griffiths and Woodgate semi-automatic rifle. This short-recoil English design was demonstrated to the British Army in 1894 and showed great promise, but met with no official encouragement.

throughout the Western world, and is still in limited use. It saw almost universal employment in Allied fighter aircraft during World War II.

While the Maxim was unquestionably the leader in the medium machine-gun field until 1917, there was also a widespread quest for a lighter automatic weapon. The advantages of the repeating rifle having been proven by the mid 1880s, it was inevitable that the thoughts of arms designers should turn to a self-loading rifle to replace the bolt-action as the soldier's individual weapon. Unfortunately, the inventor's lot was not eased by the unquestioned military obsession with long-range performance involving very powerful cartridges. During the late nineteenth century, the steels commonly used in arms manufacture were easily machined and capable of taking a fine polish, but, unless the parts concerned were of massive construction, they were not capable of sustaining the violent cycle of an automatic rifle. A 30-40 lb (14-18 kg) machine gun was much simpler to design than a 9-10 lb (4-4.5 kg) rifle.

Maxim did some work on semi-automatic rifles in the early 1880s, but preferred to specialize in machine guns. Mannlicher designed in 1885 a short-recoil rifle capable of both semi-automatic and full automatic fire, and W. Arthur, working with Schlund, patented a locked-breech rifle in England in 1885. Maxim, Mannlicher and Browning continued with rifle designs into the mid-1890s, but the two Americans tended to apply their ideas in the machine-gun field, although one of Maxim's patents in 1891 was eminently practical for rifles and was developed successfully at a much later date. Mannlicher concentrated on shoulder arms, investigating various delayed-blowback methods, but received no government favour. In 1895, he designed a gas-operated action with a locked breech.

The first semi-automatic rifle to achieve government issue was adopted by the Danish Navy and Coast-guard Service, but was ignored by the land forces of Europe. This was a 10-shot long-recoil weapon, fitted with a monopod. It was made by the Dansk Rekyriffel Syndikat, and was reasonably successful. Mauser introduced a short-recoil design in 1898 and both a long-recoil arm and a

gas-operated system in 1902. The Italian Cei-Rigotti of 1900 and Japanese Nambu of 1904 were equally unsuccessful in winning military hearts. The 1907 Swiss Trials and 1909 British trials found all automatic-rifle designs wanting. In addition to the metallurgical problem already referred to, early designers were plagued by the erratic quality of early smokeless powder. During the opening years of the twentieth century the only successful self-loading rifles were either .22-in (5.6-mm) rim-fires, or simple low-velocity medium-calibre sporting rifles, such as the blowback Win-

chester '03 and '07, using straight-sided cartridge cases, and intended for short-range deer shooting. The .351 (8.9-mm) Winchester '07 did, incidentally, see some war service in the hands of French aviators.

A greater chance of success therefore appeared to lie with a weapon somewhere between a rifle and a medium machine gun, capable of being carried by one man and of getting into instant action without being set up on cumbersome tripods. Both a cavalry and an infantry role could be envisaged for such an arm, for it could clearly give close support to rapidly advancing infantry in a

French soldiers change magazines on a Chauchat light machine gun. (The omnibus with elegant Swiss shutters is presumably for a quick getaway in case the Chauchat lived up to its reputation for unreliability.)

way that a machine gun could not. In 1903 the Dansk Rekyriffel Syndikat scored another 'first' with their 20-lb (9-kg) Madsen, a bipod-mounted weapon with a curved 25, 30 or 40-round box magazine (subsequently widely copied) mounted on top of the receiver. This arm was rapidly adopted by Danish and Russian cavalry, and over the next 50 years saw widespread use from South America to Thailand, and most places in between. Very reliable, provided rimless cartridges were used, it was also very complex. Encouraged by the Madsen's success in the Russo-Japanese war of 1904–5, Hotchkiss introduced in 1909 their 'Portatif', which weighed 27 lb (12.2 kg). This arm was given limited and unenthusiastic use by the Americans, in the guise of the 'Benét Mercie Machine Rifle', and in .303-in (7.69-mm) calibre by some Indian units.

The outbreak of war convinced all sides that automatic-rifle design would have to take second place to light machine-gun development. Britain, Belgium and Italy all adopted the Lewis, an air-cooled, gas-operated 27-lb (12.2kg) bipod-mounted gun fitted with a flat 47-round drum magazine. The weapon had been designed as a commercial venture in 1910 by an American artillery officer, Colonel Isaac Lewis, and was the first machine gun ever to be fired from an aircraft, a Wright Type B 'pusher', in June 1912. This demonstration was repeated by the designer in Belgium, and in Britain in 1913, to massive indifference. In the face of official hostility at home,

manufacture was placed in the hands of BSA. Not only did the Lewis become the standard British infantry squad gun until 1939, but it had a distinguished air career as a free-mounted observer's gun. Opinions differ over the efficiency of its design, but it was tactically and mechanically superior to any other World War I Allied light machine gun except the Madsen, and it cost only one-sixth the price of a Vickers. In 1915, Vickers were withdrawn from infantry battalions and brigaded separately, Lewis guns replacing them in ever-increasing numbers. A British battalion that set out to war with two Vickers ended it with 36 Lewis guns. The Lewis continued to serve throughout World War II, mainly as a second line, Home Guard and Merchant Marine weapon.

Germany had attempted to make a light machine gun based on its '08 Maxim. This was known as the '08/15, but was still no featherweight at over 40 lb (18 kg) with a filled waterjacket. It certainly could not compete with the Lewis for portability. Nevertheless the introduction of the Lewis and '08/15 in large quantities did begin to redress the balance and put infantry in attack at less of a disadvantage, since the new guns provided portable concentrated flanking and covering fire. An air-cooled version, the '08/18, was still too heavy at just under 37 lb (16.8 kg), and overheated badly. Two much superior designs received far less attention than they deserved, probably because they were introduced too late. These were the Bergmann MG 15 in its air-cooled

version, brought in in 1916, and weighing only 28½ lb (12.7 kg), and the DWM Parabellum, weighing 23 lb (10.4 kg), almost exclusively an aircraft gun until 1918. ·

Two French developments saw the light of day. The first, the Fusil Mitrailleur Modèle 1915, was usually known as the Chauchat after the Chairman of the four-man commission that accepted it. On the good side, it was the first military arm designed for maximum economy in manufacture. On the bad side was everything else about it. It had sloppy tolerances and jammed frequently. Its violent long-recoil action did nothing for accuracy. Much more promising was the Darne, another economy model bearing the name of one of the most prestigious of French sporting-gun makers, but whose manufacture was subcontracted to the Spanish manufacturer Unceta, today better known as Astra.

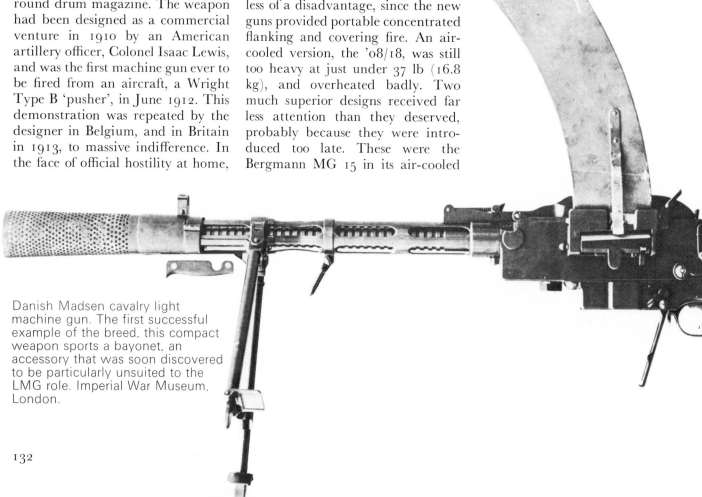

Danish Madsen cavalry light machine gun. The first successful example of the breed, this compact weapon sports a bayonet, an accessory that was soon discovered to be particularly unsuited to the LMG role. Imperial War Museum, London.

The gas-operated design is potentially very good, eschews expensive forgings, and makes use of stamped parts.

America produced a curious hybrid, somewhere between the light machine gun and the automatic rifle. This was the Browning Automatic Rifle, or BAR, a 20-shot gas-operated weapon weighing 16-20 lb (7.3-9.1 kg), depending on the manufacturer. Its magazine capacity was too small for the light machine-gun role and it weighed too much to be a successful automatic rifle. The BAR was quite complicated and expensive to make, but it was very tough and very reliable. It saw only the briefest service in World War I, in the hands of the US 79th Division, where Val Browning, the inventor's son, used it in action; but later it achieved both reasonable European popularity, being made under licence by FN, and a secure place in

Above right
The American Browning Automatic Rifle, slung for 'walking fire'. Light automatic weapons were believed to be particularly useful during the last stages of the assault. Experience showed that they were in fact more effective if used on the flank to give accurate supporting fire from a rest.

Right
The Japanese 1922 light machine gun in action in China during the Sino-Japanese War which began in 1931. This Hotchkiss-based design was over-complicated and lacked primary extraction, so required low-power ammunition and lubricated cartridge cases.

Firepower was most important when used against aircraft and here four Bren LMGs have been mounted on a Lloyd tracked carrier. Imperial War Museum, London.

the hearts of the American army.

The end of World War I saw the development of a new class of weapon, the heavy machine gun. These arms, of larger-than-rifle calibre but still more or less portable, were built in response to the increasingly aggressive role of aircraft and the more widespread use of armour for vehicles and men on the battlefield. Such arms, ranging from .5-in (12.7-mm) upwards, fall outside the scope of this book, but do reflect the increasing mechanization of warfare.

Peace left the Germans almost disarmed, with 50,000 Maxims surrendered, the British and Americans in possession of thoroughly proven and excellent Vickers and Browning medium machine guns, and everyone else rather dissatisfied with their lot.

The development of rifle-calibre automatic arms moved away from the water-cooled medium machine gun whose ascendancy had been broken by the tank and the pistol-calibre submachine gun, of which more later. More fluid tactics demanded lighter air-cooled weapons. Light machine-gun development proceeded apace in France, Finland, Japan, Russia and in a brand-new nation, Czechoslovakia, where a government-owned armament firm, Czeskoslovenska Zbrojovka Akciova Spolecnost v Brno, was founded in Brno in 1922, using expropriated German machinery and French technical advice.

France introduced the Chatellerault Modèle 1924, named after the arsenal where it was first made. Weighing slightly over 20 lb (9 kg), it married a modified BAR action with a new 7.5-mm rimless round based on Swiss and German service cartridges, and had a Madsen-inspired forward-positioned bipod and top-mounted 25-round magazine. Despite its mixed but excellent parentage, it showed

a dangerous propensity for bore explosions, and several members of a Rumanian delegation were severely injured when testing the gun in 1926. The French immediately suggested sabotage. A series of similar disasters in the hands of the long-suffering *poilus* resulted in some re-design in 1928, and the modified arm was re-issued as the 1924/29. Most problems were overcome with improved quality control and better steel.

Aimo Lahti, the brilliant Finish designer of a wide range of small arms, introduced a reliable light machine gun in 1926. This recoil-operated weapon had one disadvantage: while the barrel could be removed quite quickly, the bolt came with it. Unlike some of his other designs, this weapon did not achieve international success.

The German Army, meanwhile, had been doing some hard thinking, and had laid down a specification for a new weapons family in 1924. This comprised a submachine gun, an automatic rifle of equal ballistic performance to, and no greater size and weight than, their Kar 98k, and a light machine gun. Technical requirements included the ability to function in Arctic or desert conditions. However, Germany's financial collapse in the 1920s prevented serious development.

In Japan, a Hotchkiss-derived light machine gun, the 6.5-mm Model 1922, deserves credit as an early attempt to come to terms with the design problems involved. An air-cooled weapon, it fired from an open bolt. This means that, when the firing cycle stops, the bolt is held to the rear and no cartridge is chambered. Air can thus circulate through the barrel and the danger of a 'cook off' is eliminated. In order to facilitate ammunition supply in the field, a novel magazine arrangement was conceived by Colonel Nambu, by far the most outstanding Japanese arms designer of the period. This took the form of a hopper on the left of the action, holding six five-round rifle chargers. A ratchet mechanism fed the rounds, and the empty charger was ejected to the side. Colonel Nambu's next venture, the Type 92 medium machine gun, was a 122 lb

(55.3 kg) Hotchkiss-derived behemoth that introduced a semi-rimmed cartridge of 7.7 mm.

Light machine-gun development really got into its stride in the mid 1920s. The Czechs introduced the Vzor (Model) 26, designed by the brothers Vaclav and Emanuel Holek and by Anton Marek. This arm had a Madsen-style top-mounted magazine, a very gentle gas-operated mechanism, stainless-steel piston and cylinder, and a quick-change barrel feature. There was virtually nothing operationally wrong with this weapon or with a minor modification, the Vz 30, which was not only an immediate success with the Chinese (who made it locally), but with the Japanese, who captured large numbers, the Germans, who obtained great quantities during World War II, and the British. The British version was, of course, the .303 Bren,

A British Bren-gunner easily keeps up with his SMLE-armed comrades at El Alamein during an attack on an enemy strongpoint.

adopted in 1939 and made at Enfield, the name being derived from *Br*no and *En*field. These Czech or Czech-derived LMGs were probably the most successful weapons of their class ever made, and the Bren is indeed still in service, converted to the 7.62 mm NATO specification and better than ever. They did, however, have two serious non-operational drawbacks: they were designed for traditional manufacturing methods involving hundreds of milling operations on each gun and a high degree of engineering skill among the workforce, and they were thus very expensive and ill-suited to wartime production.

Russia had also introduced a light machine gun in 1926, although issue in quantity was not achieved until 1933. This arm was named after its designer, Degtyarev, who deliberately set out to achieve a weapon capable of rapid manufacture on simple machinery by semi-skilled labour. The arm was gas-operated, and fed its cartridges from a flat, rather flimsy-looking drum mounted

Right
The L7A2 General Purpose Machine Gun designed to fire the NATO 7.62-mm round. This weapon can be fitted onto a tripod as well as the bipod illustrated here. It has a rate of fire of 750–1000 rounds per minute.

on top of the action. While it was a good deal less refined than the Bren, it had no significant vices apart from a rather clumsy barrel change, and its outstanding performance in the Spanish Civil War convinced the Russians of its value. It remained the standard Warsaw Pact weapon until the 1950s.

Less success was achieved with self-loading rifles. The Simonov of 1936, which gave a poor performance in Spain, and the Tokarev of 1938, were designed for lightness but achieved fragility. A sturdier 8 lb 9 oz (3.88-kg) Tokarev was introduced in 1940 for issue to NCOs and, suitably equipped with a telescopic sight, as a sniping rifle. It showed real

Below
Mark I Bren guns creating an
unlikely concentration of fire in this
official British publicity photograph.

promise in the latter role, since the firer did not run the risk of betraying his position through the violent arm movements necessary to operate a conventional bolt-action.

By 1934, the German Army had lost interest in their proposed weapons system, and had concentrated on a new concept, the general-purpose machine gun. The idea was to produce a belt-fed weapon with easily changed barrels that was capable of undertaking the infantry-support role of the LMG, but could be fitted with a variety of different sights and tripod, quadrupod, anti-aircraft and vehicle mounts to suit it for almost any medium machine-gun sustained-fire requirement. The weapon adopted was the MG 34, a recoil operated gun of 26 lb 11 oz (12.1 kg) gun made by the Mauser works, although based on earlier developments by Rheinmetall's Swiss subsidiary, Solothurn. The MG 34, issued in 1936, was beautifully made, expensive, and not entirely satisfactory in the LMG role since its high cyclic rate of about 900 rpm made it inaccurate. It continued to serve widely in the Wehrmacht throughout World War II, however, and vies with the Degtyarev for the title of most-used machine gun of World War II, and the weapon subsequently saw much use in the Israeli Army.

The United States had pretty much ignored machine-gun development, but did give considerable latitude for the design of self-loading rifles to two of the best American designers, John C Garand and J D Pedersen. Garand had come to official notice by producing a self-loading rifle which was submitted to the 1920 US Army trials. He then joined the staff of Springfield Armoury. In 1922 J D Pedersen was hired to work at Springfield on both a new cartridge and a new rifle. His earlier work for the government will be covered in the submachine-gun context; he had also had a most successful career as a designer of civilian arms with Remington. Pedersen favoured a .276 (7-mm) round of less potent performance than the .30/06 (7.62-mm) US service cartridge, a concept that many designers

and military men over the last 80 years would have agreed with. His rifle was elegant, well-balanced and well-sighted, and used a toggle system rather like the Maxim and the Luger pistol.

Garand, meanwhile, had been working on a gas-operated 8-shot self-loading rifle that showed great potential. The Garand in .276-in (7-mm) calibre was adopted in 1930, but in 1931, at the insistence of General MacArthur, the Chief of Staff, the .30/06 (7.62-mm) was retained. This decision simplified supply and also saved very high re-tooling costs, since the Pedersen round was in no way similar to the .30/06. Issue to troops began in 1936, and a substantial part of the US Army was armed with self-loading rifles by the time they entered the war in 1941.

Both Italy and Japan had been introducing machine guns of no particular merit, and both nations were multiplying the number of rifle or machine-gun calibres on issue, with concomitant supply difficulties. Japan had three different 7.7-mm cartridge cases, one rimless, one semi-rimmed, one a copy of the rimmed .303 British round, and two 6.5-mm loads. Italy was issuing 6.5-mm, 7.35-mm and 8-mm.

By 1939, therefore, we find the Americans and Russians armed in varying degrees with self-loading rifles. Russia had an excellent light machine gun, but relied otherwise on old and very heavy water-cooled Maxims. Germany had the MG 34 and France the Chatellerault and a variety of older designs. Britain had its old Vickers and Lewis guns, and the excellent new Bren. Japan and Italy were armed with a variety of light and medium machine guns, few of them better than mediocre.

We must now turn to a class of automatic weapon hitherto mentioned only in passing, the submachine gun, which may conveniently be considered in isolation. As the term is understood today, this is a relatively light and portable arm, capable of fully automatic fire and chambered for a pistol-calibre cartridge. It is a one-man weapon, intended for two-handed operation.

Although both Maxim and Browning had produced pistol-calibre machine guns, this was for reasons of convenience in design or demonstration, and not to meet any defined military need. The submachine gun was spawned by the trench stalemate of World War I. The infantry rifles and light machine guns of the day were distinctly unhandy for raiding or close combat in the confines of a

Right
M 1s large and small.
Top. M 1 Garand, the United States' 8-shot semi-automatic .30/06 service rifle of World War II. *Bottom*. M 1 carbine. Despite the confusing similarity of nomenclature, this neat little 15-shot weapon fired a far less potent cartridge, and was intended to replace the pistol. Imperial War Museum, London.

Below
Beretta Moschetto Automatico of 1918. The stock and folding bayonet are typical of Italian bolt-action carbines of the period. The top-mounted magazine, missing in this picture, has certain advantages, but the system subsequently found favour only in Australia, for the Owen submachine gun. Imperial War Museum, London.

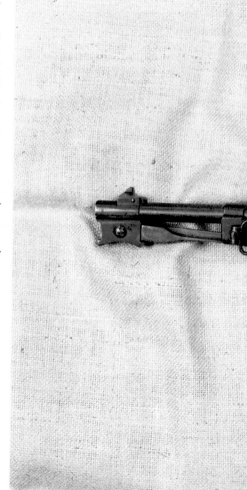

trench. A short-barrelled shotgun was awesomely effective at short range, providing the paper-case cartridges did not swell in the damp. The Americans had issued pump-action Winchester Model 97 riot guns for guarding prisoners of war, but many found their way to the trenches via such unorthodox channels of supply as stud poker, horsetrading and scrounging. The Germans protested officially that lead slugs were in breach of the Hague Convention and the pump guns had to go. Pistols were effective, but only in the hands of cool and competent marksmen. The Germans had had the beginnings of a very good idea when in 1913 they authorized the issue to field artillery, airmen and observation-post personnel of a 9-mm Parabellum pistol with an 8-in (20-cm) barrel, a detachable shoulder stock that doubled as a holster, and in 1917 a 32-round 'snail drum' magazine. Pistol/carbines with detachable stocks were nothing new, but such a large-capacity magazine certainly was. The original intention was to provide short-range firepower against cavalry, but the handy little carbine was

the perfect companion for uninvited nocturnal visiting across no man's land.

In the meantime, the Italians had developed a curious little double-barrelled weapon, the Villar Perosa, also known as the Revelli, after its designer. This was a twinning of two 25-shot 9-mm Glisenti-calibre submachine guns, each with a cyclic rate of about 1,500 rounds per minute despite their delayed blowback system. Since each magazine, perched atop its barrel, could be emptied in one second, and since many Villar Perosas were issued without benefit of sights of any kind, the double configuration at least supplied the shooter with a second chance before reloading. This strange device was used somewhat optimistically as a light machine gun to equip aircraft, cars and motor-cycles. In the assault, however, it was mounted on a wooden tray which was slung around the firer's neck.

Without doubt, the Villar Perosa was a false start along the road to true submachine-gun development. Its action was modified by Tullio Marengoni, an outstanding arms design-

er working for Beretta, and a single-barrel version equipped with a conventional carbine barrel and stock was named the Moschetto Automatico 1918. Marengoni was responsible, in whole or in part, for every Beretta submachine-gun design until his retirement in 1956. The new weapon was very successful in the hands of the Italian *arditi* (assault troops).

In Germany, Hugo Schmeisser was engaged in concurrent but entirely independent development. In 1917, Bergmann manufactured his design, a 9-mm weapon with a wooden stock, using the 8-in (20-cm) 'Artillery' Parabellum barrel and 32-round 'snail drum' magazine mounted on the left-hand side. This simple blowback weapon, known now as the Maschine Pistole 18.1, was at first frequently referred to as a 'muskete'. 'Muskete' and 'moschetto', like the English 'musketoon', mean 'small rifle', and reflect the thinking behind the Beretta and Bergmann. In 1918, the mechanical problems inherent in the design of light, handy rifle-calibre shoulder arms had by no means been overcome and, with one unsuccessful

exception, attempts at such arms had ended up larger, heavier, clumsier, more complex and less reliable than manual repeaters. By employing a low-pressure pistol cartridge, the problems were sidestepped, and a compact reliable weapon with great short-range firepower was easily achieved, but at the sacrifice of long-range effectiveness. The Germans managed to get some 35,000 into the hands of their troops for the spring and summer of 1918. They equipped small groups trained to move rapidly, act independently and exploit surprise. These new tactics very nearly broke the Allied line, and, like the British tank, ended the ascendency of the medium machine gun.

The Beretta and Bergmann were not the only attempts to achieve short-range concentration of fire during World War I. The Steyr M 12, a sturdy, exceptionally powerful Austrian automatic pistol, was adapted to selective full-automatic fire and provided with a double-capacity magazine of 16 rounds. Although they must have been uncontrollable in full automatic fire, a few Steyrs seem to have found their way into the hands of the Brandenburg Grenadiers, who were among the most effective German shock troops.

J D Pedersen adopted a radical approach to the problem, a dual-function rifle. A 'device', known officially as a 'pistol' to confuse the enemy, replaced the bolt in a slightly adapted '03 Springfield, P.17 Enfield or Moisin Nagant (all on issue to US forces), and instantly converted it to a 40-shot semi-automatic. At the behest of General Pershing, in command of American troops in France, 500,000 were ordered, but

none of the 65,000 produced by the war's end saw action, and the Pedersen device was scrapped on the grounds of weight and the danger of losing the rifle's bolt.

By 1919, all the main characteristics of the submachine gun and nearly all the practicable methods of operation had been developed, but with the Armistice, military interest died. Armouries were stuffed with superbly made rifles that would meet all future needs, military budgets were pared down to essentials, and no sane politician could publicly contemplate future wide-scale conflict.

The unorthodox submachine gun was admitted to have some application as a police weapon, and the Allies permitted a surprisingly generous issue of one Bergmann per 20 German police, but forbade its use by the miniscule German Army. Such small requirements as existed in other armies were met by Bergmann designs made under licence in Belgium and Switzerland. Buyers included turbulent China, the Japanese Navy, and Finland. The submachine gun suited the lightly armed Finnish ski troops fighting at short range in forested terrain. Like the Turks in earlier years, they could not afford to be complacent about Russia. Aimo Lahti, their very successful designer of arms for below-zero temperatures, produced his first, rather ponderous, over-complex submachine gun in 1926, but followed it with the Suomi 1931. This simple, beautifully made 9-mm arm could be equipped with 20, 40, 50 or 71-round magazines. It achieved a reputation

for great reliability and good accuracy to 300 m, and was adopted in due course by Sweden, Norway, Denmark, Switzerland and the Polish police. The Finns fitted bipod rests to some of their guns, and their massed-fire techniques profoundly affected Russian design thinking and tactics during the Winter War (1939–40).

Although there was no official German Army interest in submachine guns after the mid-'20s, German manufacturers were seeking ways to circumvent the strictures of the Treaty of Versailles. Rheinmetall purchased the Swiss firm of Waffen-fabrik Solothurn in 1929, and then used Solothurn to acquire the huge Steyr arms factory in Austria. Both factories produced the Steyr Solothurn submachine gun in the early '30s, which was based on a design by a German, Louis Stange. A sound and well-made arm, resembling the Bergmann but housing its recoil spring in its wooden butt, it was purchased by Chile, El Salvador, Bolivia, Uruguay, China and Japan, and adopted by the Austrian Army in 1934.

If the Suomi and Steyr-Solothurn achieved limited success, the only other important design of the 1920s, the Thompson, very nearly did not. Colonel, later Brigadier-General, John Taliaferro Thompson was a career ordnance officer convinced of the need for an automatic rifle. He formed the Auto Ordnance Corporation in 1916 to produce a blowback rifle fitted with a 'hesitation lock' designed by a naval commander called Blish. This employed a wedge

in an inclined groove that jammed and locked the action under high pressure but slid out of engagement when the pressure dropped to a safe level. In 1917, Thompson was recalled to war service, but design continued. It soon became clear that the Blish lock would not work with rifle cartridges unless they were oiled, since the violent opening of the action tended to tear them in half. The .45 (11.4-mm) US service pistol round, would, however, work without lubrication. Thompson began touting the idea of a 'trench broom', but the 'Persuader', the first of a luridly named series of prototypes, kept jamming in tests. By 1918, a version dubbed the 'Annihilator' showed promise, but the Armistice killed hopes of quick profit. General Thompson persisted, and the handsome outcome was the Model 1921, which boasted a detachable butt and an enormous clockwork 100-round drum magazine. Despite favourable US Army and Marine tests, a wide-

ranging European tour produced only one piece of business. Auto Ordnance received a mysterious order for 495 guns, which were delivered to a freighter in Hoboken, New Jersey. General Thompson had cause to doubt the tenet that 'all publicity is good publicity' when the proud purchasers were revealed to be the Irish Republican Army. His appalling bad luck worsened when the 'Tommy Gun' supplanted diamond-buttoned spats as the status symbol of the successful gangster both on and off the silver screen.

The Thompson 1921 possessed an almost uncontrollable cyclic rate of 800 rounds per minute, but the US Navy showed interest, which spurred further development. The result was the Model 1928, with a reduced cyclic rate of 600–725 rounds per minute, and an optional but almost universally fitted extra, the 'Cutts Compensator'. This device was a muzzle brake, with slots to direct emergent gas upwards, the jet effect countering

Above
The Thompson submachine gun fired the .45 (11.5-mm) ACP cartridge which could be fed in from magazines holding 20, 30, 50 or 100 rounds.
Top. Model 1928 A 1.
Bottom. Model M 1.
Pattern Room, Royal Small Arms Factory, Enfield.

Above right
Two of the best submachine guns made.
Top. Italian Beretta Model 38A 9-mm submachine gun made to the highest standards of finish.
Bottom. German MP 40, the first of the economy model 'ugly ducklings' made of cheap and easy stampings, but a highly efficient combat weapon nevertheless. Imperial War Museum, London.

the recoil at least to some degree.

By 1938, Auto Ordnance had sold only 10,300 guns and was near failure. Apart from miniscule US Naval and Marine purchases, only China had shown serious military interest. BSA had been licensed to make the design, but no European orders had been forthcoming. War was looming in Europe, and the Thompson was finally adopted by the US Army, so General Thompson was able to raise enough money to save his company, but at the cost of his own control. He died in 1940, and did not see his gun's success. Tough, and available in large numbers, it armed the British and French after Dunkirk. By the end of wartime production in 1944, 1,383,043 had been

made. Just nine days of peak war production were needed to equal the entire sales of 17 peacetime years. Thompsons are still in production in America, in a variety of models, and the romantic old relic is enjoying the longest production span of any sub-machine gun made.

US Marines had successfully used Thompsons in the Nicaraguan jungle in 1927, and Steyr Solothurns and possibly Lahtis saw service during the Gran Chaco War of 1932–35 in South America. Then came the Spanish Civil War (1936–39), which allowed the Russians, Italians and Germans to field-test new equipment and ideas in a brutal war of fluid tactics and much close-quarter combat. Although the worsening Euro-

pean political situation had encouraged arms design, submachine guns had veered towards mechanical over-complication. The simplicity of the Bergmann had been abandoned in favour of such dubious benefits as the 'hesitation lock' of the Swiss MKMO of 1933, the variable rate of fire of the Czech ZK 383 or the 'hesitation lock' and variable-rate mechanism of the Spanish Star 35 series. None was successful, and the events in Spain underlined the military virtues of strength and straight-forwardness.

In a classic year, Beretta introduced their Model 1938, one of the last and probably the best of the first-generation carbine-style submachine guns, expensively machined from

German MP 38 submachine gun, fitted with a muzzle cap to prevent foreign matter entering the bore.

good steel and walnut. Over the years it passed through a number of essentially cosmetic changes, in the interest of manufacturing ease, but was still in production in 1970. It is notable both for its two-trigger arrangement, the front for semi-automatic fire, the rear for automatic, and for a major improvement in box-magazine efficiency. Though neither short nor light, the Beretta has all the advantages in action. It points well, is easily controlled and is accurate. Bought by at least 14 countries, it received the signal honour of being adopted by the post-war West German Border Police in preference to German designs.

The other introduction of note was the German MP 38, the first of a new generation. It had a folding metal stock, it was compact and devoid of wood, just the weapon for paratroopers and tank crews. Like the 1935 pattern steel helmet and the jackboot, it radiates an aura of cold, hard Teutonic efficiency. The MP 38 had been developed as a commercial venture by Erma, based on mainspring designs of Vollmer. Although dubbed the Schmeisser by the Allies, he being the only German submachine-gun designer of any international repute, this was a misnomer, since he had no hand in its creation. Spanish experience and Panzer promptings caused a sudden Wehrmacht change of heart, and the MP 38 was adopted as the best available design. Its main drawback was that it was extremely expensive to make, requiring many milling cuts and much aluminium. A year of total war dictated the appearance of the MP 40, almost identical in operation and appearance, but designed for rapid economical production using stamped metal, simple brazing and spot welding. Scarce aluminium was eliminated, cheap carbon steel employed wherever possible, and resin-impregnated paper was used for the highly practical stocks.

The MP 40 ushered in a new era of cheap, crude, disposable arms, often assembled from parts obtained from widely scattered subcontractors. While the erratic Chauchat LMG was the first military weapon designed for inexpensive, rapid mass production, the MP 40 proved that economy could co-exist with efficiency. Over 1,047,000 were made up to the end of production in 1944, and output was not significantly affected by Allied bombing.

World War II was the submachine gun war. At its beginning, there were perhaps 50–60,000 in the world; at its end, 10,000,000. It was ideal for paratroops, partisans and Commandos, compact and cheap to make and to feed. Britain, desperate for arms after Dunkirk and daily expecting invasion from the skies, saw the despised 'gangster gun' in an entirely new light. Everything shootable was purchased in America, a proven submachine gun was put into manufacture in England, and a search was begun for a new mass-production design. The submachine gun selected for English manufacture was the Bergmann in its MP 28 II guise, in which a simple box magazine supplanted the complex 'snail drum'. Named the Lanchester after the man who slightly anglicized it, the gun was put into production by Sterling Armaments Co. and was embellished with a solid-brass magazine housing, a splendidly retrogressive extravagance that must have endeared it to its only user, the Royal Navy.

The new design was the Sten, its name an acronym of Major R V *S*hepherd, in charge of the Small Arms Group, H J *T*urpin, the designer, and *En*field. Four marks of this simple 9-mm weapon were eventually issued in quantity, a total of 3,750,000 being made during the war, two million of them Mark IIs.

There was considerable and justifiable consumer resistance at first, for the gun was prone to accidental discharge and jamming. 'Stench gun' was among its more printable nicknames. The main fault was not with the gun itself, but with the magazine, which seems to have been Lanchester /Bergmann-inspired, but execrably

Four versions of the Sten gun.
From top to bottom.
Mark I, with a wooden fore end and forward folding wooden pistol grip.
Mark II, its butt and barrel easily removed for rapid packing or concealment.
Mark III, which has a pressed receiver and was designed and made by the toy-making company Lines Bros.
Mark V, essentially a well-made Mark II. The forward pistol grip was often omitted.

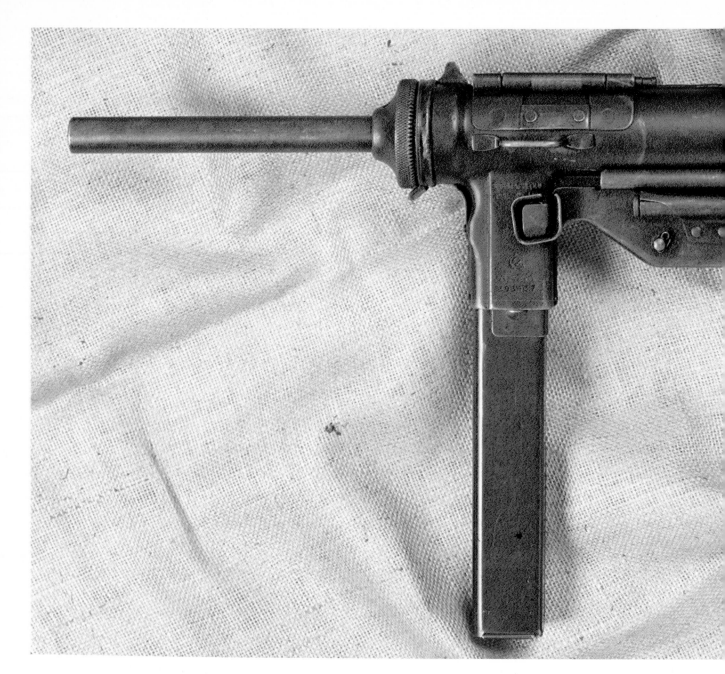

rendered to poor tolerances in soft steel. Despite improved quality control, the Sten's reputation for unreliability was never entirely dispelled, but the Mark V (the Mark IV was never issued) was a sound and quite well-made weapon. The Sten was copied in resistance workshops in Denmark and Norway from plans dropped by the Allies, and modified versions and exact reproductions were also produced by the Germans in the last months of the Reich. Its manufacturing processes influenced the design of the American M3 'Grease Gun', and it was also made after the war in China. The Mark II S, a silenced version, was a popular clandestine weapon and the only

muffled submachine gun to achieve real success in World War II.

Russia also required guns in a hurry. It had issued two designs by Degtyarev, its premier machine-gun designer, in 1934 and 1940. These were essentially derived from the Bergmann MP 28 II, chambered for the Russian 7.62 mm pistol cartridge, itself borrowed from the 7.63 mm Mauser 96 pistol, and fitted with a Suomi-style, 71-round drum magazine beneath the barrel. Following Japanese practice, the interior of the barrel and chamber was chrome-plated. This reduced wear, prolonged barrel life, helped prevent the bottle-necked cartridge case from sticking and, in the days of corrosive

Above
US Army replacement for the Thompson 1928 submachine gun: the stamped metal M 3 'Grease Gun', made by General Motors at one-sixth the price of the Thompson.

Right
These members of the Danish Resistance Movement during World War II are raiding a German cycle store. One holds a Sten gun, many of which were supplied to the Danish and other Underground movements by the Allies, usually by parachute drop. One resister appears to be armed with a Bergmann Bayard automatic of 1910.

Assembly line for Russian PPSh 41 submachine guns.

priming compounds, obviated the need for cleaning. By 1942, faced with an overriding demand for quantity not quality, a crude but still wisely chrome-lined mass-production version was introduced, the PPSh 41, "PP" standing for *pistolet pulemet*, or machine pistol, and 'Sh' for Shpagin, another successful arms designer. Over five million were made during the war, and the PPSh 41 was subsequently copied in Korea, Hungary, China and, in a somewhat modified version, in Iran.

Russia was faced with almost insuperable problems in training and supplying her huge but inexperienced and frequently badly officered armies. The PPSh 41 symbolized an entirely new approach to infantry: the 'tank rider' battalions. These simple, sometimes savage men had only one tactic, to ride on and run behind the tanks into battle. The T-34 tanks provided the mobility and shock, their parasite infantry mopped up and occupied any ground gained. The tank riders lacked either the equipment or the training for the complex mutual support and interaction between infantry, armour and artillery that existed in a Panzer unit. Their losses were appalling, but by sheer numbers and courage short-range aggression achieved success.

We have seen how the exigencies of warfare affected arms manufacture

in England and Germany, and spurred the adoption of mass-production techniques hitherto almost unknown in the very conservative small-arms industry. It is, however, true to say that the pressure was greatest on Germany, and that the Allies, with safe industrialized havens in America and Canada, could afford to get by using tried and true methods. When Rock Ola, the juke box company, and IBM started making carbines for the US Government, they made them the old way. While almost any factory could make cheap submachine guns, nearly all Allies mass-manufacture calibre rifle designs such as the BESAL, a BSA-developed LMG capable of production with minimal machinery, remained at the prototype stage, held in reserve in case of massive damage to traditional plant.

The circumstances of the war forced the Germans to investigate radical techniques. The Johannes Grossfuss company, experts in metal stamping, were asked to produce an economy arm that performed the same general-purpose function as the MG 34. Their designer, Dr Grünow, was not only highly competent technically, but thoroughly realistic, since he was a trained machine-gunner. The result, the MG 42, outdid all expectations. Not only was it cheaper than previous models, it was better. Dr Grünow adopted the Polish Stecke lock, a simple roller-bearing system of great mechanical smoothness. The belt feed was also far less violent, although the rate of fire had been stepped up to 1,200 rpm, and the design has been copied in current Belgian, British, American and Swiss GPMGs. The design is still in very widespread use in 7.62-mm NATO guise as the MG 3.

By 1940, Germany had decided that she must introduce a self-loading rifle. Both Mauser and Walther in 1941 offered expensive designs employing the standard 7.9-mm service cartridge, but neither was very successful. In due course Walther did produce the Gew 43, a much-simplified version owing more than a little to the Russian Tokarev gas system. This rather roughly finished arm had a built-in mount for a telescopic sight, and served mainly as a sniper's weapon. Of far greater interest was the Fallschirmjäger-gewehr 42, a multi-purpose arm chambered for the standard 7.9-mm service cartridge, and adopted by the Luftwaffe-controlled paratroopers. They had been mostly armed with submachine guns in Crete, and had received a severe mauling from British riflemen as a result. When used as a semi-automatic, the FG 42 fired from a closed bolt, for accuracy, but in fully automatic fire it utilized an open bolt, to assist cooling. It also introduced the 'straight line' stock with separate pistol grip. Unfortunately, despite its highly futuristic appearance, it was quite expensive, and its fate was sealed by the mutual antipathy between the Luftwaffe and the Wehrmacht, who by this time had very different concepts of what a rifle should be.

The Wehrmacht wanted a rifle with a large magazine capacity chambered for an intermediate cartridge, effective up to 400 yd (366 m) or so, cheap to make, easy to use, and controllable in fully automatic fire. These arms were needed to counter the Russians, whose myriad submachine gun-armed troops had shown a disturbing tendency to favour hand-to-throat combat. The combination of frozen fingers and five-shot bolt-actions was doing nothing for German morale. After much political wrangling, this emerged as the 'St G 44' the initials standing for *Sturmgewehr* or 'assault rifle', to signify a hoped-for new spirit of aggression that it would engender on the Eastern Front. The rifle, despite being a trifle overweight at 11 lb 4 oz (5.1 kg), did everything expected of it, although it was never available in sufficient quantities, and the 'assault rifle' name of this type of intermediate-cartridge weapon has stuck ever since.

Meanwhile, the Americans issued

the M 1 Carbine, whose light weight, large magazine capacity and low recoil made it a runaway success, over 6 million of all versions being made. Intended as a safer and more effective replacement for the pistol hitherto issued to junior officers and specialists, it fired a 108-grain .30 bullet at only 1900 fps (579 mps), which made it a miserable man-stopper. Despite a long post-war career, particularly as an arm for women and light-framed Asiatic troops, the M 1 carbine was really a blind alley in the overall history of shoulder arms.

During the final year of the war, Germany produced a number of very clever minimal-cost, minimal-manu-facture designs, but of a level of crudity and shortness of service life that made them suitable only for emergency use. Germany's real in-fluence on arms design was in three fields: the general-purpose machine gun, the assault rifle, and low-cost, decentralized mass production.

The principal Russian assault rifle, the AK 47 or Kalashnikov, a 30-shot weapon with a straight-line stock, weighing around 9½ lb (4.3 kg), and fitted with a 16.3-in (41.4-cm) chrome-lined barrel, was introduced two years after the war. This very efficient rifle, which has few and insignificant vices, has come to sym-bolize the freedom fighter and the terrorist. Minor variants are made in most Communist countries, and also in a more radical modification in Finland. The action also provided the inspiration for the Israeli Galil.

A series of light machine guns has been developed to use the inter-mediate round, the present model being the RPK, a long-barrelled, bipod-mounted version of the AK, capable of taking a 75-round drum. This is complemented by an out-standing general-purpose machine gun, the PK, which combines an en-

Variants on the Kalashnikov assault rifles.
Top. Rumanian AKM, similar to the Russian mass-production AKM, but fitted with a forward handgrip.
Bottom. Chinese Type 56, almost identical to the AK 47.
Pattern Room, Royal Small Arms Factory, Enfield.

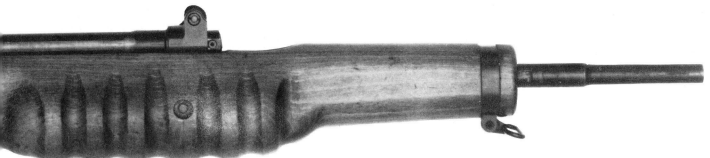

Above
British EM 2 rifle. This very
compact experimental design places
the firing action next to the
shooter's cheek, and the positioning
of the ejection part makes it
unsuitable for a left-hander. A
simple optical sight is mounted on
the carrying handle.

Left
L1 A1 rifle, the British version of the
FN. This example is fitted with a
grenade-launching sight, and is
accompanied by an 'Energa' anti-
tank grenade and a practice
grenade. On recently produced
versions, the wooden furniture has
been replaced with nylon.

Below
German MP 44. The low barrel line
of this German assault rifle gives a
direct thrust into the shoulder,
minimizes muzzle climb and
disturbance of aim, and allows a
quick second shot. The ribbing on
the stamped metal body of the gun
provides rigidity.

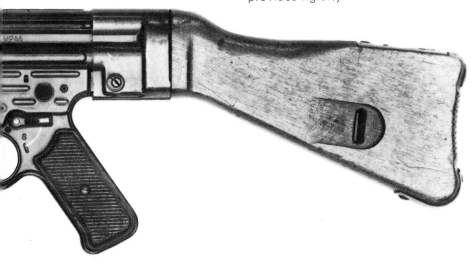

larged Kalashnikov action with an interchangeable barrel, belt feed and the old, rimmed 7.62-mm rifle round of 1891, which gives it range.

In the West, the course of development has been anything but smooth. After the war there was a rush of machine-made self-loading rifles such as the Belgian FN Model 49 (in fact a pre-war design), the 7.5-mm French MAS 49, and the Swiss SK 46. The French rifle was an excellent and economical arm, but they were all too long, too heavy and too powerful. Britain wished to adopt an intermediate calibre weapon, the extremely compact EM 2. This employed a 7-mm cartridge of very advanced design, giving a much better short and medium-range ballistic performance than the Russian round. The rifle itself was a thoroughly radical, optically sighted 'bull-

pup' design, which eliminated the butt stock, placed the firing hand in front of the magazine, the cheek against the action, and combined a $24\frac{1}{2}$-in (62.2-cm) barrel with an overall length under 3 ft (91.4 cm). The designers were Czech expatriates, however, and the arm exemplified the traditional Czech drawback, being far too costly to make.

The creation of the North Atlantic Treaty Organization has resulted in a long and financially crippling series of attempts at standardization, each subverted by chauvinism, economic selfishness or politics. In 1953 it was agreed that the member nations would adopt the same cartridge. America carried the political and financial clout, but her deeply conservative Army could see no further than a 20-shot Garand, made on old Garand machinery, and using a slightly shortened version of the old .30/06 M 2 cartridge. The results were the M 14 rifle and the 7.62-mm NATO cartridge, a fine deer cartridge, a superbly accurate target-shooting round, but still much too big, too heavy and too powerful. In today's rapid, highly mobile warfare troops need small, light cartridges and rifles, so that they may carry many more rounds for the same overall load, and thus increase their chances of causing enemy casualties before having to be supplied. Most other NATO nations, including Britain, adopted the Belgian FN Fusil Automatique Léger (FAL) of 1950, and many African and South American countries followed suit. Dubbed 'the mechanical musket' by some British military wit, its robust qualities are reflected in its weight and length, and it is a clumsy weapon for snap shooting. It is also built to last, at a price to match.

Stamped steel weapons.
Top. The little Czech .32 (7.65-mm) Skorpion submachine gun. It can be carried in a shoulder holster and fitted with a silencer. Made of metal pressings, it functions poorly with substandard ammunition.
Bottom. West German 7.62-mm Heckler & Koch G 3. Currently one of the most widely distributed Western military rifles, this example was made for Saudi Arabia. Imperial War Museum, London.

American assault rifles.
Top. M 3 carbine fitted with an infra-red sight.
Bottom. Armalite AR 18, a design intended for easy mass production on simple machinery, which has been manufactured in the United States, Japan, the Netherlands and Britain.

Assault rifles of today and yesterday. *Top.* Swiss SIG 7.62-mm self-loader with forward folding bipod. *Bottom.* One of the first in the field – the German 7.9-mm MKb 42, which entered service in 1942.

Those nations that did not opt for the FN have shown great interest in the German Heckler and Koch G 3, a thoroughly modern pressed-steel rifle derived from the Spanish CETME which itself was the product of expatriate Mauser engineers who had been working on the St G 45. The weapon is a delayed blowback, with an extremely violent ejection of fired cartridge cases, which become a real hazard to others in the vicinity. NATO non-cooperation has now reached the point where the nominally standard 7.62-mm cartridge is produced to such a variety of national specifications that some rifle/cartridge combinations are now incompatible.

If World War II marked the zenith of the submachine gun's importance as a military weapon, it also heralded its decline. The introduction of the German MP 43, parent of the St G 44, which produced effective performance up to 300 m and was capable of fulfilling both a rifle and a submachine-gun role, underlined the weakness of pistol-calibre arms, capable only of short range and poor penetration.

While armies cling to the 7.62-mm NATO or other full-power rifle cartridges, there exists a place for a pistol-calibre submachine gun. Indeed, since the war there has been a third generation of submachine guns. These arms have tended to become ever more compact, but more controllable in fully automatic fire, through the use of the so-called 'wraparound' or 'L' bolt. In first and second-generation weapons, the entire mass of the bolt lies behind the barrel. In third-generation weapons, most of the mass of the bolt in its forward position is over, or surrounds, the barrel. Not only does this enable the overall length of the weapon to be minimized, but the system, probably invented in 1944 by an Italian, Giovanni Oliani, lessens changes in the centre of gravity created by the reciprocating breech-block. Among the weapons using this system are the Israeli UZI, a particularly rugged arm now made under licence in Belgium and issued in West Germany and to the United States Secret Service, and the futuristic Beretta Model 12.

Faced with strong competition from light, short, compact high-performance rifles, submachine guns have tended to shrink still further, becoming small enough to be carried in hip holsters or even shoulder holsters. In Czechoslovakia the .32 Skorpion is issued to tank crews and line-of-communications troops, as is the slightly larger and more effective 9-mm Wz63 in Poland. In the United States Gordon Ingram introduced his Model 11.380 (9.6-mm) ACP and Model 10 9-mm Parabellum or .45 (11.4-mm) ACP. These exceptionally small and rugged arms enjoy a certain vogue in bodyguarding circles and as counterweights for frogmen. In truth, however, when the shooting starts the effectiveness of such arms tends to be in inverse proportion to their size.

In the future, the submachine gun will probably be most effectively deployed as a police or internal-security arm, where its poor penetration is a positive asset in crowded cities. Since high precision also helps reduce the chances of injured innocents, interest has again been shown in weapons firing from a closed

Left
Negev Bedouin vote under the relaxed gaze of an Israeli policeman armed with an UZI submachine gun.

Below left
French police receive instruction on the MAT 49 submachine gun. This 9-mm weapon, widely used by French military, security and police forces, has an excellent reputation for strength and reliability. When not in use, the magazine and its housing may be folded forwards and upwards to be underneath the barrel.

Stoner M 63 made by Cadillac Gauge, which features interchangeable barrels, mounts and feed systems on the same action, thus allowing the same basic unit to be turned into anything from a submachine gun to a tripod-mounted GPMG, and the Armalite AR 18, now made by Sterling Armaments in England. The excellent AR 18 fulfils exactly the same tactical role as the AR 15, but is manufactured using stamped metal rather than an expensive forged receiver. The Royal Small Arms Factory at Enfield has designed the 4.85-mm Individual Weapon. This echoes the 'bull-pup' design of the 1950s EM 2, but is really designed for cheap and easy production. Its cartridge, the 4.85 mm, is based on the .223 in (5.56 mm) case, but has a far more stable bullet giving better penetration than the parent round. However, recent improvements in bullet design for the 5.56 mm have substantially reduced this advantage.

It is almost certain that the current NATO trials will opt for the improved 5.56 mm round as a NATO standard. It is rather less certain that a single design of rifle will be chosen, particularly as the United States already possesses several million M 16s and several European rifles are arguably superior. Russia is also pursuing a small-bore round, and it is likely that whichever designs are chosen will arm the two great power blocs for the next 20 years.

breech, such as the Heckler and Koch 9-mm MP 5, where the aim is not disturbed by the slamming forward of a heavy breech-block when the trigger is pulled.

Meanwhile, deep in the Vietnam jungles, the United States was finding out that the M 14 was no match for the AK 47 in close combat. Matters were not helped by the poor level of weapon training and appalling marksmanship displayed by the average GI. The Americans turned to the only available indigenous weapon that bore any resemblance to an assault rifle, the Colt AR 15. After initial difficulties were overcome, these stemming from an un-

suitable propellant in some batches of ammunition and from incorrect weapon training, the AR 15, subsequently renamed the M 16 for military purposes, served very well, and convinced the United States that a new NATO cartridge and rifle was required.

Excellent little rifles in .223 in (5.56-mm) calibre have been produced by Beretta in Italy, Heckler and Koch in Germany, FN in Belgium and Israel Military Industries. The French have adopted a cartridge and 'bull-pup' rifle of their own design, the MAS 5.56-mm. Eugene Stoner produced two other series of 5.56-mm weapons, the

Ammunition

David Penn

Sir Nicholas Crispe fully equipped as a musketeer and holding a match and rest in his left hand. Across his chest is a bandoleer containing measured charges of powder.

A firearm is a means of transferring energy from the weapon to a more or less distant target. It is the lineal descendant not of the bow, which delivers very little energy and kills primarily by causing haemorrhage, but of David's pebble and sling. The 'fire' in a firearm does not cause trauma directly, but imparts energy to a projectile.

Until the mid-nineteenth century, the only practicable means of propulsion for a firearm was 'gunpowder', also known as 'black powder'. This is a mixture of two highly inflammable fuels, charcoal and sulphur, to which is added saltpetre, an oxygen-rich chemical that allows the two fuels to explode without need for air. Half the products of gunpowder are hot gasses that occupy far more space than the solids they originate from, most of the remainder being deposits of sooty fouling. By exploding gunpowder in a confined space, huge gas pressure is developed. In a firearm, the projectile represents the line of least resistance, like the cork in a champagne bottle, and the pressure drives it from the barrel.

Gunpowder probably reached Europe from China sometime during the thirteenth century. By the 1320s,

Right
Powder horn made in late sixteenth or early seventeenth century. It has a simple cut-off device fitted to the nozzle, and the sides have an engraved scene, possibly representing St George and the Dragon.

Left
Selection of late sixteenth-century powder flasks
From top to bottom
Unusually shaped flask of ebony with a metal cut-off. It bears the arms of Saxony.
Hemispherical flasks for priming powder, inlaid with horn and fitted with mounts.
Wooden priming-powder flask with silver medallion set in the side.

cannon were recorded in the Low Countries, England and Italy, and it was clear that metal projectiles were being made for them. Artillery featured in the Battle of Metz in 1324, and 'crakeys of war' were in operation during Edward III's invasion of Scotland in 1327.

Until about 1450, black powder, then known as 'serpentine', was pretty unreliable. The proportions of ingredients varied widely, no doubt reflecting relative availability as much as the whim of the producer. The chemicals were simply stirred together, after being finely ground. This was less than satisfactory, since if continually agitated, for instance by pack-horse transport, the constituents separated because of their different specific gravities, and had to be re-mixed. There were sometimes failures to ignite if the powder

was packed too tightly, which indicated that the fine powder had eliminated air. The strength of powder grew over the years as the proportion of saltpetre was increased. Charcoal quality was also critical, correctly carbonized alder, beech or dogwood being found the most satisfactory.

By the mid-fourteenth century, military demands had resulted in a degree of mass production of powder. The first recorded water mill was in Augsburg in Germany. To reduce the fire hazard and probably also to prevent the fine-grained powder 'meal' from being blown around by air currents, the chemicals were damped during manufacture. This resulted in a big lump, or 'cake' of very well integrated powder. It was soon discovered that this process had two very beneficial by-products, since

it prevented the separating of the ingredients, and, when broken up into the size of a grain of wheat, the powder had much better burning characteristics since air was retained between the grains. This type of powder was known as 'corn' powder. By 1546, Venetian records show a proportion of ingredients for muskets of 48 parts saltpetre, 8 parts charcoal and 7 parts sulphur, which closely approximates to the modern mix, although this was not generally adhered to in Europe until the late seventeenth century.

At first, the shooter carried his bullets in a pouch, his propellant corn powder in a horn or flask, and a smaller horn of fine meal powder for priming. By the mid-sixteenth century the bandoleer had appeared. From this cross-belt were hung on short cords 12 or so little metal or leather-covered wooden containers each containing a single powder charge. These rattled horribly, and were occasionally ignited by the musketeer's match. By 1590, paper or linen cartridges made by winding strips around a mandrel or cylindrical core and containing both powder and ball, had begun to make their appearance, the word 'cartridge' being derived from *carta*, the Latin for paper. The Swedish Army led by Gustavus Adolphus (reigned 1611–32) was the first to adopt a standardized cartridge, each man being issued with 12, which gives a fair indication of the expected expenditure of ammunition during a battle. Cartridges were carried in reasonably weatherproof boxes or pouches, and the improvement in powder quality allowed a separate priming flask to be dispensed with. These innovations in cartridge technology increased musket fire from one round every $1\frac{1}{2}$ minutes to two rounds per minute.

Until 1720, there was little improvement in projectile type, the round ball being in almost universal use. Shot in varying sizes had begun to be used in Italy by about the middle of the sixteenth century, and multi-projectile shot loads very quickly became general in Europe for 'fowling' and small-game shooting where the spread of shot improved the chances of a hit. During the eighteenth century large shot known as buckshot also received some military use, either alone or combined with a full-calibre ball, a load particularly favoured in America. Projectile quality improved, however, with the ever-increasing use of metal bullet moulds in place of stone, made to ever more exact tolerances. Not that exact tolerances always mattered much, since most smooth-bored weapons were loaded with an undersized ball, to ease the problem of ramming a projectile down a fouled barrel. This 'windage' made it impossible to ensure that the ball left the muzzle precisely along a line coinciding with the axis of the bore. In the Brown Bess musket this difference was considerable, the bore being a nominal .753 in (19.1 mm),

'Roman candle' wheellock carbine. A group of barrels was so arranged as to discharge a series of shots one after the other, in a continuous volley.

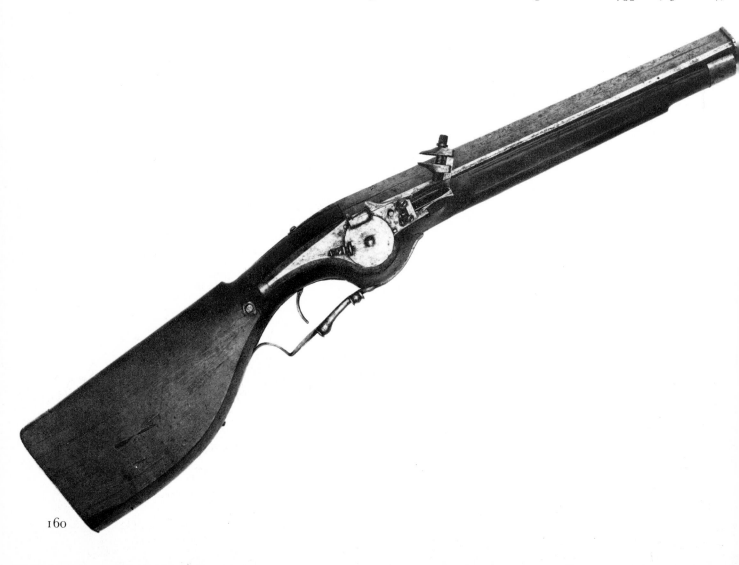

and the ball about .69 in (17.5 mm).

In rifled arms, however, a close fit between bore and ball was essential, and until the early nineteenth century bullets were a tight fit and hammered down into place – hard work which distorted the ball out of true and adversely affected its accuracy. Alternatively, a lubricated patch of leather or textile was interposed between an undersized ball and the barrel. This latter technique was Swiss or German in origin, and was common knowledge by the 1740s, if not in common use, since it was an infuriatingly finicky business to prepare and centre the patch, particularly in combat.

In the 1720s the 'belted ball', a round ball with a substantial lead collar around its circumference, was developed in Spain. This belt was mechanically made to fit in deep, two-groove rifling, and thus allowed the use of a slightly undersized ball. The system eventually enjoyed a certain vogue in the second quarter of the nineteenth century, but had a poor reputation for long-range accuracy. By the 1720s it had also been proved that round balls were inferior ballistically to oblong elliptical projectiles, but these observations saw little practical application until the nineteenth century.

The main improvement in ammunition during the eighteenth century was in powder. Heavy-duty screw presses were developed to increase the density of the powder 'cake', and corned powder was polished and given a light coating of 'meal' powder in a successful attempt to reduce friction and a rather less successful attempt to minimize the substance's sensitivity to moisture. Powder manufacture became less of an art and more of a science, and in 1756 an attempt was made in France to produce a smokeless powder by eliminating sulphur entirely, but without success. In 1775 Antoine Lavoisier, one of the founders of modern chemistry, was appointed director of the French Gunpowder Commission. He introduced the drum system, in which the constituents were ground separately in revolving iron barrels or drums by the impact of free-rolling bronze balls. They were then combined in a copper drum and corned in a wooden barrel. The result was a far higher degree of consistency in manufacture, thus making possible quality control.

Lavoisier's system was taken to America by Eleuthère Irénée du Pont de Nemours, an expatriate Royalist who had begun working in the French royal powder manufactory at the age of 17. Du Pont set up his factory in 1804 on 'foaming Brandywine's rough shores', and the excellence of his 'Eagle' powder provided the foundation of one of the great American industrial empires. The main advance in gunpowder technology during the early nineteenth century was in the more perfect purification of the saltpetre.

Chemical fulminating mixtures based on gold were known in the seventeenth century, and in 1788 Comte Berthollet produced a silver fulminate in France. Experiments began immediately to use this as a propellant, but it was far too sensitive and violent. Instantaneous detonation caused a sudden liberation of gases and the bursting of the gun barrel. In 1799 Edward Howard produced a fulminate of mercury that was slightly less hazardous to manufacture, but was otherwise just as hard to tame. At about this time, a major improvement was made in the production of shot for game shooting. Small shot for game had been made by pouring molten lead through a sieve held just above water, which cooled the metal. The results were nearly always tear-drop shaped, however, and did not fly true. On 10 December 1782 William Watts took out a patent for making 'small shot solid throughout and perfectly globular in form'. The process, which apparently came to him in a dream, was to drop the molten lead from a considerable height. A shot tower was built on the South Bank of the Thames in 1789.

By 1805, Rev Alexander Forsyth had produced his successful percussion lock, in which fulminate was used for ignition only and not as a propellant. Forsyth's invention is discussed at greater length in Chapter 1, and it is only necessary here to mention that his development of fulminate as a means of ignition rather than propulsion encouraged the invention of the percussion cap. It is not entirely certain who first invented the copper percussion cap, although the earliest known written reference is Prélat's French patent of July 1818. Prélat, however, specialized in importing English guns and patenting any new features he could discover on them. He had already registered in 1810 a copy of the Forsyth lock patented in England in 1807. His 1818 patent covers five types of fulminate ignition, also including pill locks, tube locks and patch locks, all of which are known to have appeared earlier in England or America.

Between the second decade of the nineteenth century and the 1860s there was considerable activity, mainly among French civilians, to develop the self-contained cartridge for breech-loaders. In England and America and among the French military, interest centred on percussion ignition, and ballistic research concentrated on the improvement of projectiles for muzzle-loading rifles that combined ease of loading with accuracy and a long-range capability.

Samuel Pauly's cartridge, first patented in France on 12 September 1812, was self-contained with a fulminate pellet in its 'head', metallic (in its pistol form) and obturating. The gas-tight effect was obtained not by the expansion of a thin-walled case to grip the sides of the chamber, but by using a tapered, rimmed case in a tapered chamber, thus obtaining a mechanical seal. Shotgun versions used a similar obturating metallic 'head', but with a paper tube in front containing powder and shot. The priming fulminate, nestling in a cavity in the rear of the cartridge, was ignited by a striker, but the heat and violence of its explosion caused undue wear and tear on the mechanism. In his British 1816 patent, Pauly got around this problem by igniting the fulminate with a jet of air superheated by blowing it at high pressure through a small aperture. This worked quite well, and the idea was indeed revived for the Daisy-Heddon 'case-

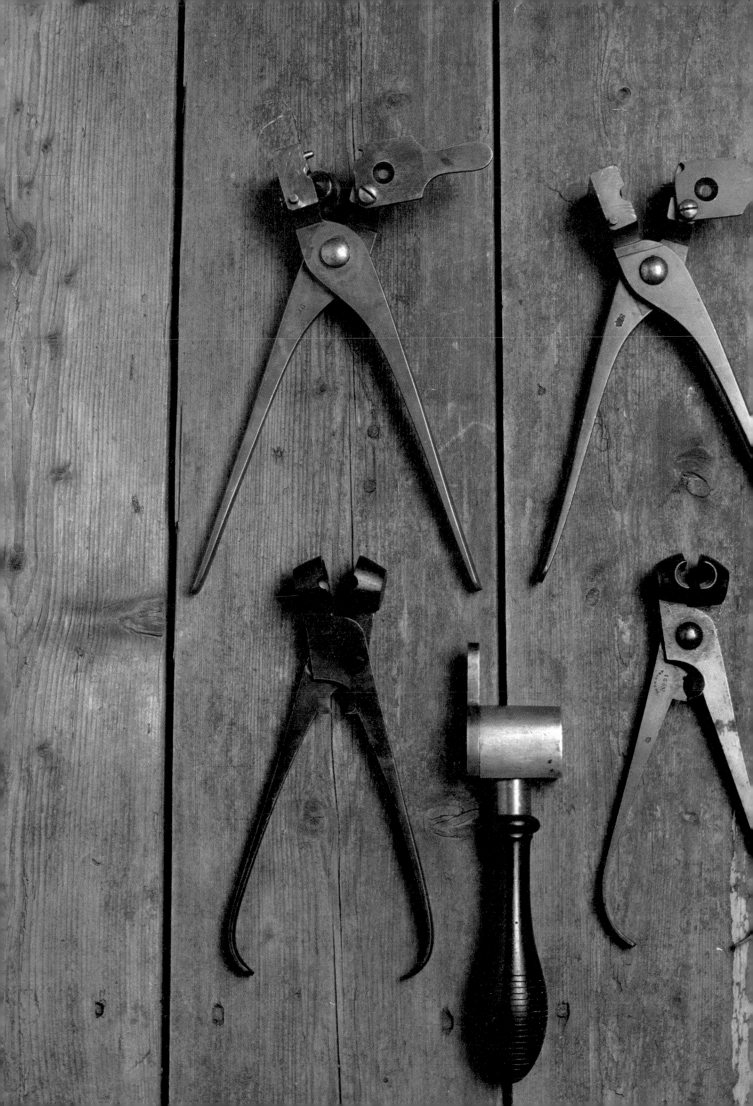

less cartridge' of the 1960s. In later versions, a conventional cap and nipple were attached to the rear of the Pauly cartridge.

In 1826, Galy-Cazalet received a French patent for an inside-primed centre-fire parchment cartridge case. This was not gas-tight, and was not a success. In 1831, Robert took out a French patent for a primed case, with the priming extending across the entire head of the case. This developed into the Flobert 'bulleted breech caps' of 1849, which, when applied to low-powered indoor 'saloon' rifles and pistols, created something of a 'craze'.

In 1839, Lefaucheux patented the pin-fire cartridge, in which a paper cartridge was equipped with a brass head, from the side of which protruded a pin. When struck by the weapon's hammer, this was driven downwards to strike a percussion cap. When improved by Houllier's patent of 1846, which reinforced the head and gave the cap proper support in a recessed base washer, the pin-fire became the first efficient cartridge suitable for widespread, cheap mass production. Although it was practicable only for low-pressure loads, it enjoyed wide popularity for shotguns and cheap revolvers until after World War I.

In 1848, Hunt patented his 'rocket ball' in the United States, in which the powder charge was contained in the base of a hollow projectile. Although there is no doubt that he considered himself the inventor, the idea had been patented twice before in England, in 1841 by Hanson and Golden, and in 1847 by Steven Taylor, but both designs remained in obscurity. Smith and Wesson had patented a metallic base-fire cartridge in 1854, but technical difficulties forced them to pursue the 'rocket-ball' line of development until their 1860 patent, which was for a true rimmed cartridge and really no significant advance on Houllier's design. Their rim-fire quickly caught on in America and by 1864 a wide range of low-velocity rim-fires from .22 in (5.58 mm) to .69 in (17.5 mm) were in evidence. The copper cases of early rim-fire ammunition obturated well, but they were much too

Bullet moulds from the period 1840–65.
Top. Two moulds for cylindro-conical, hollow-based rifle bullets.
Bottom. Two conventional round-ball moulds and an unusual one-piece rifle mould for the Jacobs rifle. The mould on the right is marked 'IMPROVED' since it has a deeper pouring hole to allow the lead to fill the mould-cavity better.

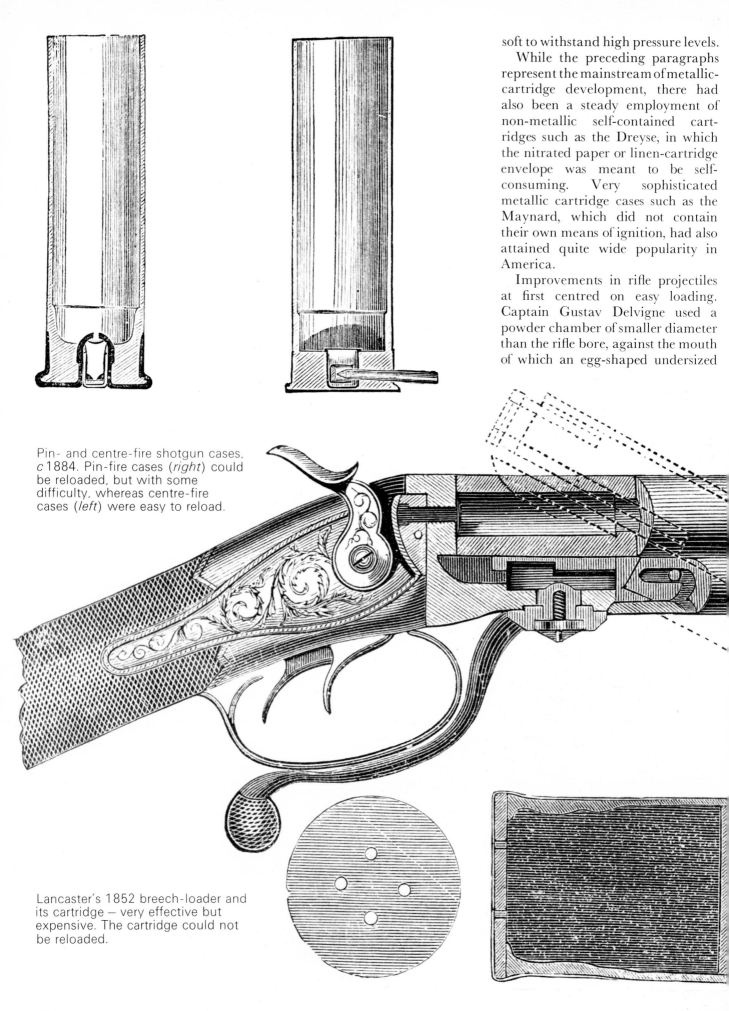

soft to withstand high pressure levels.

While the preceding paragraphs represent the mainstream of metallic-cartridge development, there had also been a steady employment of non-metallic self-contained cartridges such as the Dreyse, in which the nitrated paper or linen-cartridge envelope was meant to be self-consuming. Very sophisticated metallic cartridge cases such as the Maynard, which did not contain their own means of ignition, had also attained quite wide popularity in America.

Improvements in rifle projectiles at first centred on easy loading. Captain Gustav Delvigne used a powder chamber of smaller diameter than the rifle bore, against the mouth of which an egg-shaped undersized

Pin- and centre-fire shotgun cases, c 1884. Pin-fire cases (right) could be reloaded, but with some difficulty, whereas centre-fire cases (left) were easy to reload.

Lancaster's 1852 breech-loader and its cartridge — very effective but expensive. The cartridge could not be reloaded.

projectile could be swelled out to bore size by brisk pounding with a ramrod. This did little for accuracy. His fellow Frenchman, Colonel Pontcharra, suggested an undersized egg-shaped ball and a sabot, which showed an improvement, and in 1834 was used to equip a crack French rifle regiment, the Tirailleurs de Vincennes. This was improved upon by Colonel Thouvenin, who incorporated a *tige*, or pillar in the breech. Powder lay around this, and it served as an anvil against which an elongated projectile was rammed until it expanded to bore size. It was difficult to clean, and bullet distortion was bad for accuracy. Finally, Captain Minié, working with Colonel Thouvenin, developed an undersized conical bullet with a hollow base containing an iron cap. The explosion of the powder blew the iron cap forward, which expanded the tail of the bullet to grip the bore. The system was an immediate success.

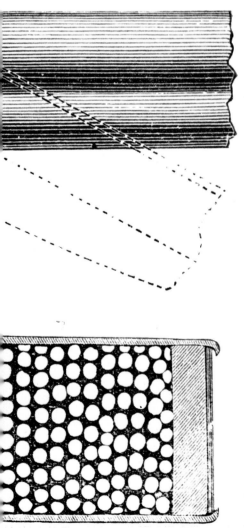

being adopted by France and Belgium in 1849, and by Britain in 1851 in an inferior form which performed badly. In 1853, with the adoption of the .577 Enfield, the British took into service the 'Pritchett', a very satisfactory projectile based on precepts laid down by Metford. While Minié deserves every credit for achieving the adoption of the hollow-based cylindro-conoidal bullet, it should be noted that the British Army had tested and rejected essentially similar systems submitted by Captain Norton in 1823 and the gunsmith William Greener in 1836.

During this period a further significant advance took place in bullet manufacture. Hitherto, projectiles had been cast from molten lead, with the attendant problem of minor variations in weight and imperfections in balance caused by air bubbles. In 1843 Napier's compressed-bullet machine introduced the 'cold swageing' process in which bullets were formed by intense pressure. The results had much greater consistency and a lower failure rate.

In 1846 nitroglycerine, the first successful alternative explosive to gunpowder, was discovered by an Italian, Sabrero. A colourless liquid formed by the action of nitric and sulphuric acids on glycerine, it is a highly unstable chemical compound capable of almost instantaneously rearranging itself into stable gaseous compounds of far greater volume – accompanied, of course, by a big bang. It is so sensitive that it will explode if disturbed, and it is extremely hazardous to manufacture and use. As a propellant, it was a non-starter, since its pressure peak was reached instantaneously. In 1846, Schönbein discovered that the action of nitric and sulphuric acids on cotton or other cellulose produced a very clean burning, smokeless 'cotton powder' that might be suitable for small arms or artillery. A slightly different version, dubbed optimistically 'gun-cotton', was almost immediately tried in rifles with catastrophic results. The results were, however, measurably less cataclysmic than with pure nitroglycerine, new hope was kindled, and all Europe was soon echoing to the sound of

exploding powder works and bursting gun barrels. Particularly disastrous explosions in 1847 at the Faversham powder mills in Kent and at a French plant cooled official interest except in Austria, where General Baron von Lenk continued to experiment, with little practical success, although his rank did ensure that a group of field artillery batteries were equipped with gun-cotton cartridges.

In 1863, Frederick Abel, working at the powder mill at Waltham Cross, England, improved manufacturing techniques of gun cotton to a point of reasonable safety. A successful propellant was finally achieved by a Prussian, Captain Schultz, in 1864–5 using tiny disks of nitrated wood. This was a 'bulk' powder, of approximately equivalent volume to an equally powerful charge of gunpowder, but its fierce burning temperature proved highly erosive to rifling and its pressure curve suited it best to shotgun use. Shotgun powder has to peak quickly, when sustained by the relatively heavy breech, but must drop for the rest of the shot's travel through the thin-walled barrel. Gentleness is also required if good shot patterns are to be obtained. 'Schultz' enjoyed great popularity well into the twentieth century.

Following the work in 1847 of Dr Hartig, of the Brunswick Forestry Service, it was more generally appreciated that it was possible to dissolve gun cotton in an ether/ alcohol mix to produce a 'colloid', a toffee-like sustance capable of being moulded. Between 1870 and 1875 Frederick Volkmann patented a powder called 'Collodin' in Austria. He discovered that by varying the process of manufacture he could control the rate of combustion with precision. Unfortunately, the Austrian government decided Volkmann was presenting a serious threat to their gunpowder monopoly, and closed his works in 1875. The first successful rifle powder was therefore French, not Austrian, the Poudre 'B' developed by Paul Vieille and adopted in 1884. This set the ball rolling in every sense of the term, and there was widespread investigation to achieve safer manufacturing

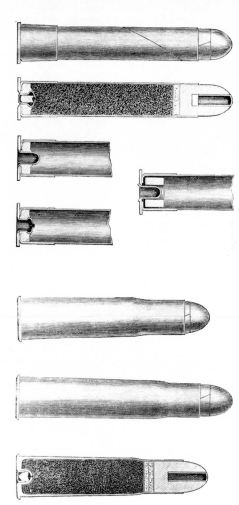

Solid-drawn and rolled brass
cartridges with paper patched
Express bullets, c 1880.

methods and a degree of stability of
performance in climatic extremes.

These first nitrocellulose propel-
lants are today known as 'single-
base', because of their single active
ingredient. Alfred Nobel produced a
'double-base' explosive in which
nitrocellulose and nitroglycerine
were combined. This was further
developed by an Explosives Committee, with Abel, now a baronet, as
president. The result was 'cordite', so
named because it was extruded in
long thin strands. It was more stable
than Poudre 'B', but was also extremely erosive to barrels. There
now exists a wide range of both
single and double-base powders for
every purpose, over fifty being available on the American commercial
market. The main improvements
have been in safety of manufacture
and the development of coating
compounds to retard further the
speed of burning. The only other significant change was the introduction
by Winchester of 'ball' powder. This
globular propellant is easy to measure
and pour, and thus consistent to
load. It is also economical and safe to
make, since almost the entire process
takes place under water.

In 1868 the American Union
Metallic Cartridge Company began
to manufacture 'solid drawn' brass
cartridge cases designed by Berdan.
These were much stronger than any
copper case, or any form of composite case such as the Boxer, used for
the Snider and Martini-Henry rifles.
They could thus withstand much
greater pressures, and had the added
advantage of being reloadable. Solid
drawn brass cases, with either 'Boxer'
or 'Berdan' forms of external primer,
have remained the standard until the
present day. Steel cases have been
given widespread military use in the
twentieth century; the economy and
availability of the material out-
weigh its poor obturation and violence to rifle chambers. Plastic cases
have received only very limited and
specialized use for rifle and pistol
ammunition, but have widely replaced paper cases for shotgun use.

We have seen how the introduc-
duction of smokeless powder resulted
in the need for a reduction in bore
size and the need to use a harder

Group of rifle cartridges, including
the Martini Henry with its brass
case (*third from right*) and the very
powerful Kynock 600 (*fourth from
left*) used for big-game shooting.

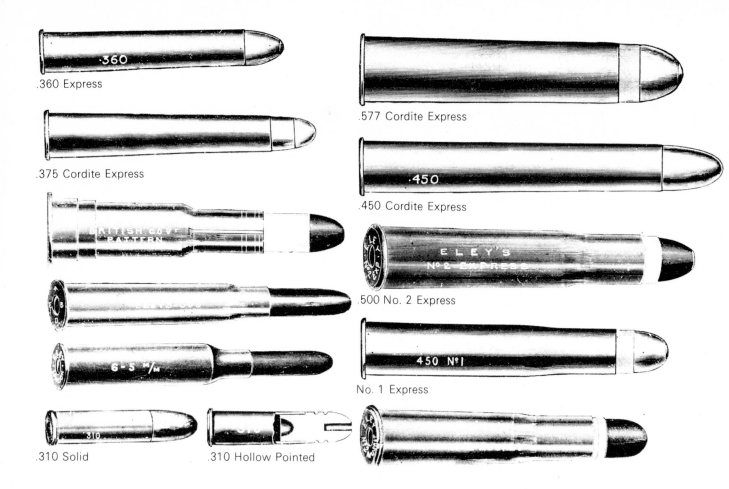

.360 Express

.375 Cordite Express

.577 Cordite Express

.450 Cordite Express

.500 No. 2 Express

No. 1 Express

.310 Solid

.310 Hollow Pointed

During the latter part of the nineteenth century many cartridges were designed for specific targets. High-powered express cartridges ensured a flat trajectory for bullets for big-game shooting. Cordite, a smokeless propellant, derives its name from its thin, stick-like shape.

bullet material than lead, in order to avoid stripping. Although the French had opted for a solid bronze projectile, most nations preferred to clad a lead core in a hard envelope. The favourite material was cupro-nickel, an alloy that seemed to combine just the right qualities of resilience and ductility. As faster and faster loads were developed in the late nineteenth and early twentieth centuries, however, there was a great increase in cupro-nickel fouling in the barrel, deposited as rough 'high spots' that were ruinous to accuracy. They could be removed mechanically by polishing with a mild abrasive, but were a thoroughgoing nuisance. An alternative, ferrous metal, was cheap and malleable, but rusted unacceptably. It was discovered that the addition of tin eased the problem, and success was finally achieved with an alloy of copper, zinc and tin known as 'Lubaloy', developed by the Western Cartridge Company, and made in England under licence by Nobel as 'Nobeloy'.

The German Commission rifle of 1888 marked the first wide-scale adoption of the rimless cartridge case. Hitherto, most cases had a rim or flange to aid extraction and to position the case correctly in the chamber. The rims, however, made feeding from a box magazine difficult, especially if the rim of the uppermost cartridge was incorrectly positioned behind the rim of the cartridge below. This caused a most effective jam. The rimless case fed smoothly, but was more expensive to make. Both types had their advantages and at the turn of the century it was quite common in England and Europe for sporting cartridges to be made in both flanged and rimless versions.

Although the Hague Convention effectively precluded the use of any but full-jacketed bullets for military purposes, the apparent lack of knock-down power of the small-bore high-velocity rifle was of great concern to the sportsman. A fully jacketed bullet could result in wounded game which, if it eluded the hunter's attempts to follow it up, was condemned to permanent injury or a lingering death. To ensure an instant and humane kill, a profusion of soft-

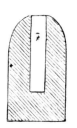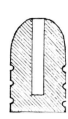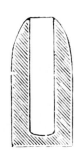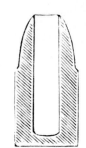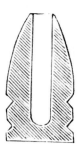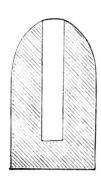

Types of Express rifle bullets, c 1885.

nosed, expanding bullets have been developed, some designed for almost instantaneous mushrooming on light, soft-skinned game, others for a combination of deep penetration and bone-smashing capability, coupled with some degree of expansion, to deal with heavy antelope or soft-skinned dangerous game. Very large calibre full-jacketed bullets, referred to as 'solids' in sporting terminology, remain necessary for elephant, rhino and Cape buffalo, whose horn-boss possesses an impressive reputation for impenetrability.

The change from black powder to smokeless brought another unlooked-for and unwelcome side-effect. Ignition difficulties resulted in an increase in the quantity of priming compound, which contained potassium chlorate. On firing, this became potassium chloride, akin to table salt, very sensitive to moisture and prone to produce rapid and severe rusting in any but very dry conditions. The sooty fouling of black powder had actually provided a remarkably protective barrier against the potassium chloride, which was washed out by the water usually used to remove powder fouling. Since smokeless powder left little fouling, riflemen neglected to wash out the bore, which had been thoroughly exposed to a large dose of the rusting agent. Amazingly, the reasons for the corrosion were not understood until the publication in 1922 of a US Federal investigation prompted by problems encountered during World War I. Rheinische Westphalische Sprengstoff had announced a 'rust-free' primer in 1901, but incorporated ground glass in the priming compound. Any target shooter who used 'Rhen-West', which had a high reputation for accuracy, could reckon on having to re-barrel his rifle every season. In 1911, the 'R' (for *Rostfrei*) primer was marketed in Germany. This eliminated the ground glass but introduced a new and almost equally effective abrasive, barium carbonate. Remington introduced its 'Klean-bore' priming in 1927, but this tended to become insensitive with age and was affected by high humidity, so most American and British military cartridges continued to be loaded with corrosive primers until after World War II.

Since 1945, improvements have mainly been in precision and in cooler-burning, less erosive powders. Immediate and meticulous cleaning after shooting is a thing of the past. The target shooter can buy off the shelf .22 or centre-fire ammunition capable of grouping under $\frac{1}{2}$in (12.7 mm) at 100 yd (91.4 m) and the hunter can purchase a cartridge specially tailored for anything from rats to rhinos. The greatest changes have been in shotgun cartridges, the plastic shotshell having become commonplace. Although waterproof, it is not bio-degradable, unlike its paper predecessor, which must count as a defect. The old system of felt and card wads has been replaced by plastic wads, usually incorporating a 'shot cup' to prevent contact between shot and bore. This stops deformation of the lead pellet, so the shot flies true, making a tighter and more regular pattern. Indeed, the improvement in patterning has gone too far for some tastes, and the Russians are now loading old-fashioned felt-wadded cartridges, devoid of shot cups or shot collars, to open up the patterns again for skeet shooting, a fast, close-range form of clay target competition.

There has also been a resurgence of interest in nineteenth-century single-shot rifles and cartridges for hunting and target shooting, and long-obsolete arms are again in production. It is again possible to buy, brand-new and very probably made in Italy, a Springfield cavalry carbine, a Browning single-shot, a Remington Rolling-block, a Martini or a Sharps 'Old Reliable' buffalo rifle, and to shoot it with all the pleasure but few of the problems that great-grandfather experienced, since there is even a safe, smoky but otherwise clean substitute for black powder called Pyrodex. A plethora of new wheellock, flintlock and percussion muzzle-loading weapons enjoy even wider popularity, and today's amateur can span the centuries in a morning's shooting.

Manufacture
and Proof

David Penn

The Jack of all trades, we are assured, is master of none, and, with rare exceptions of genius this is true. The history of manufacturing has been very much the history of specialization. Running concurrently with this development has been a steady improvement in precision, in which the arms-making industry has often taken the leading role.

The first cannon and small handguns were the products of the blacksmith and bellfounder. Simple stave stocks or 'tillers' were within the capability of anyone able to wield a hand axe and a sharp knife. Matters began to change somewhat with mechanical developments during the fifteenth century. Even the simple matchlock had to be let into the wooden stock, which was itself taking on a more complex shape. Skilled joiners began to play a part, and specialization had begun. Although the occasional finely decorated European matchlock of high quality does occur, almost all these weapons were workaday and utilitarian. The wheellock presented so many tactical advantages that it was an immediate success, but only among those capable of affording such a complex mechanism.

Wheellocks were so expensive that they were decorated as a matter of course, often very extravagantly. They were the composite creations of barrel makers, locksmiths, stock

Butt of a wheellock sporting gun showing typical fine-quality inlay on the walnut stock. The contoured trigger guard is also typical of these weapons.

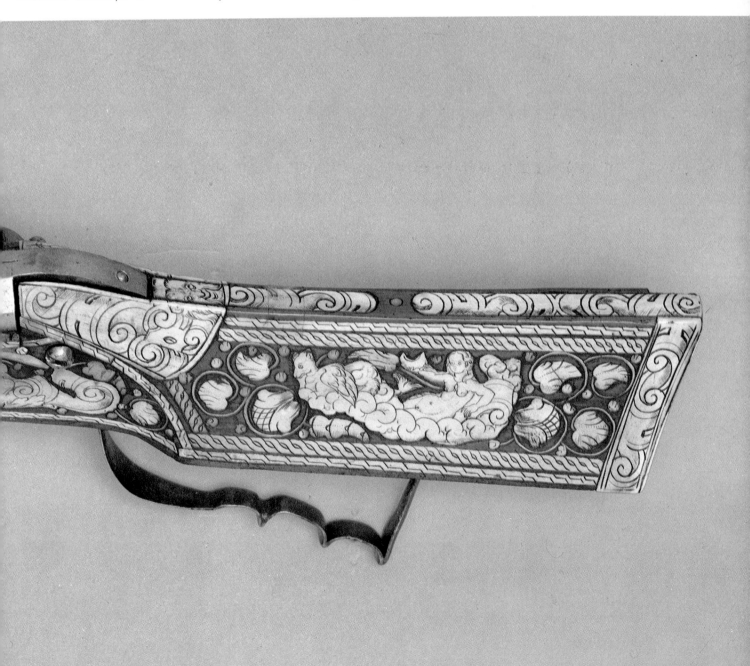

carvers, inlayers, etchers and engravers of metal, gilders and enamellers. Great artists such as Holbein and Dürer produced designs for decorating wheellocks. When rifling became reasonably widespread in central European sporting weapons of quality during the mid-sixteenth century, this again encouraged specialization in the manufacture of gun barrels.

In areas where the guild system was strong, it was only to be expected that gunmaking would eventually establish its own protective trade society. It was quite usual for such guilds to demand that an apprentice be capable of manufacturing a complete firearm of an acceptable standard, often in miniature, before he was recognized as a Master. In those days, leadership was from the front in

Below left
Detail of inlay work on the stock of a wheellock hunting rifle, showing the intricacy (and expense) of the work.

Below and bottom
Designs for the decoration used on the butts of wheellock rifles, drawn up *c* 1580. Victoria and Albert Museum, London.

Right
Page from an eighteenth-century illustrated encyclopedia showing the components and construction of a flintlock.

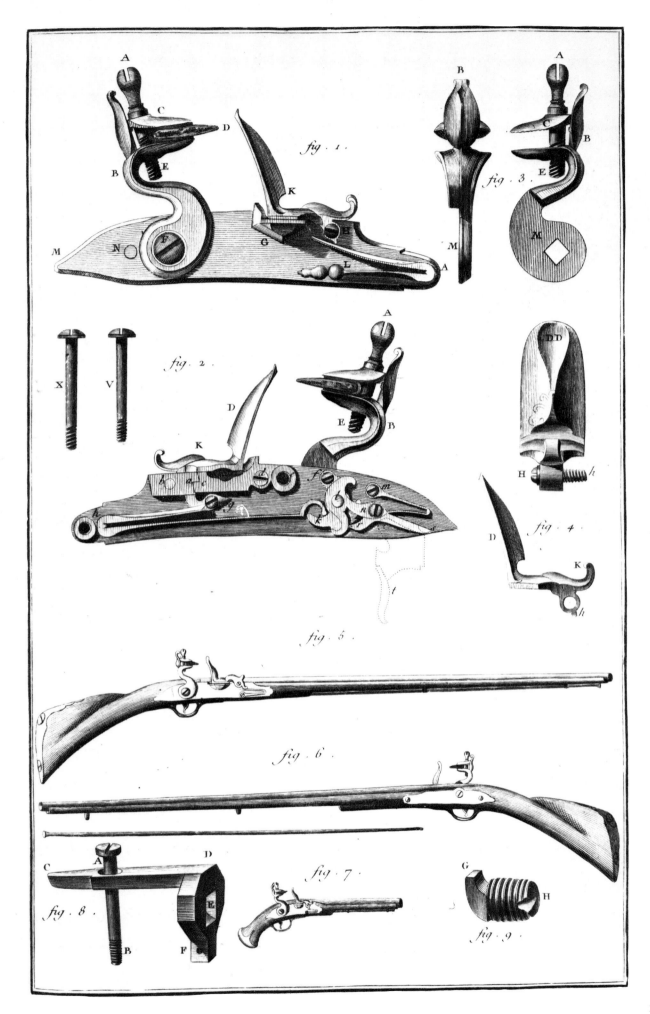

fig. 1.

fig. 2.

fig. 3.

fig. 4.

fig. 5.

fig. 6.

fig. 7.

fig. 8.

fig. 9.

Superimposed-load wheellock. The two locks are mounted on a single plate, and the first shot was discharged by the front lock.

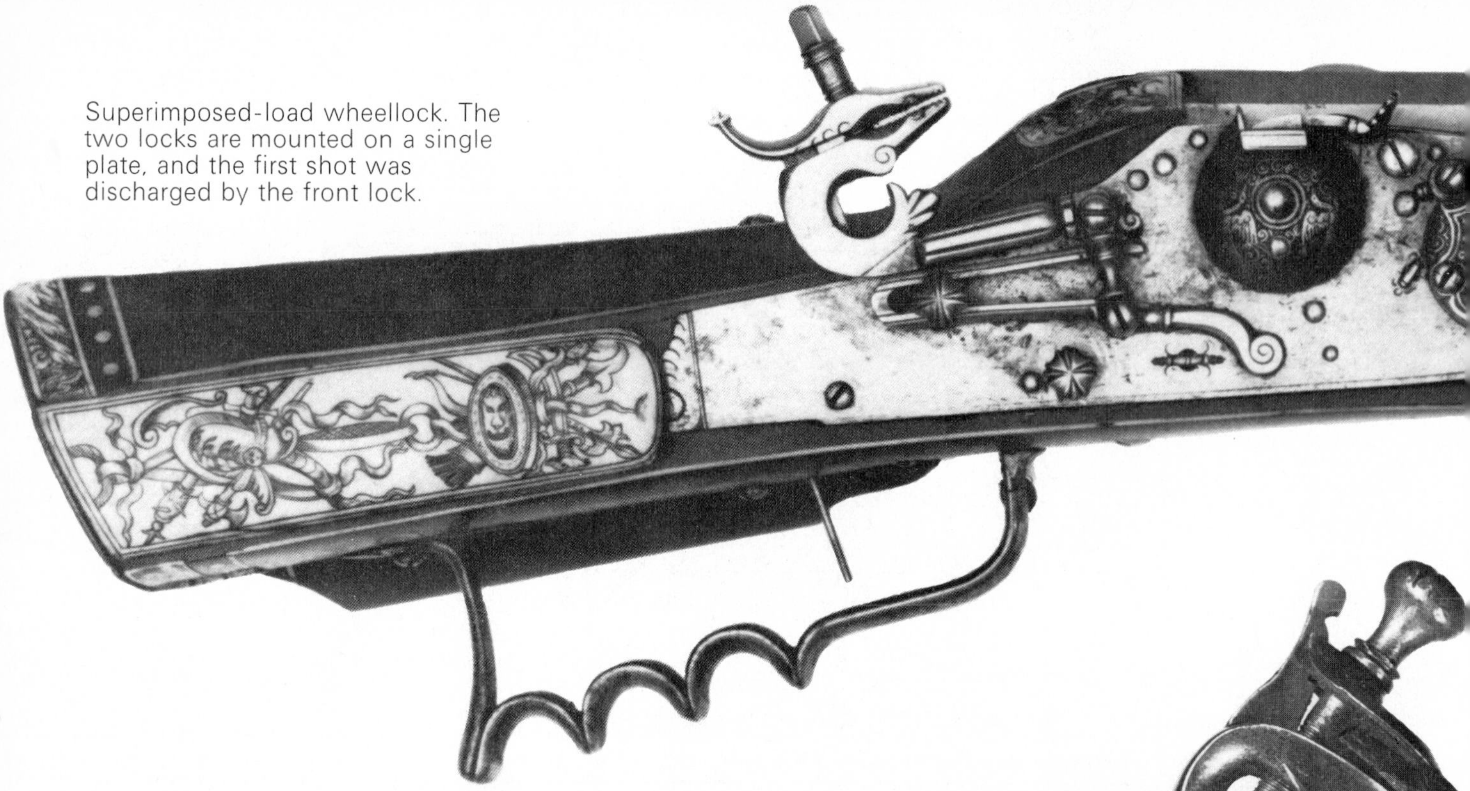

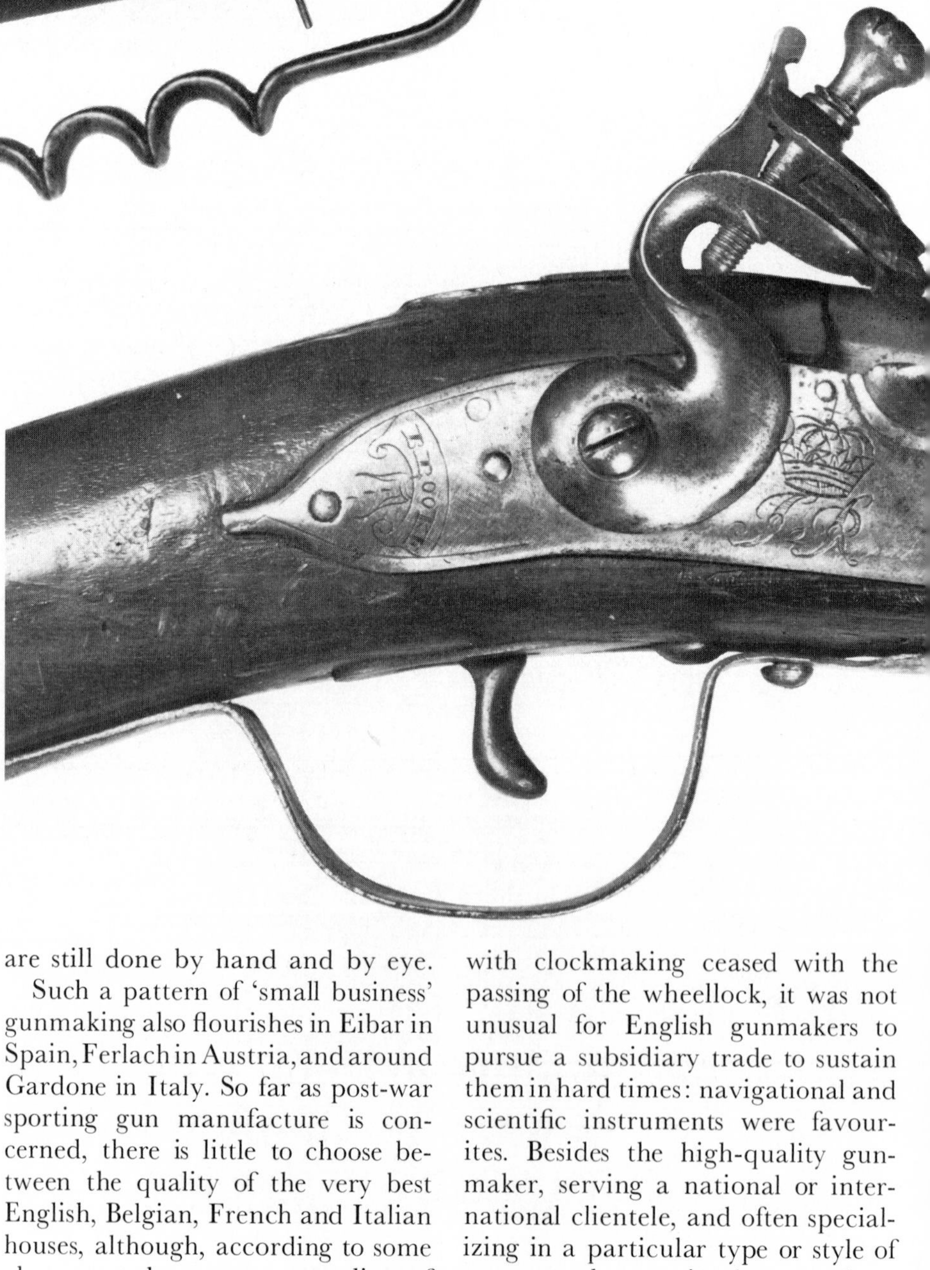

manufacturing matters as well as military ones, for unless the Master was himself a technician of a high order, he had not earned the right either to criticize his workers' efforts or to hand on the skills of his trade to the next generation of apprentices. Nevertheless, in day-to-day business, the Master would tend to specialize. He and his workforce would complement each other, and would, if necessary, buy special skills or products from elsewhere.

With modifications, this pattern of production has continued to the present day for the production of 'best' sporting guns, made to order and by hand. There are still proprietors of gunmaking establishments, such as Ian Crudgington of Bath or John Wilkes in London, who are capable of making unaided an entire 'best' shotgun, but they do not really need to do so. Nor would it be a very economic means of production. Most such firms are run by businessmen who employ highly skilled specialist actioners, barrelmakers, finishers and stockmakers. Most such work has become 'light industrial' in that labour-saving devices like steam-driven, and later electrically powered, lathes, band saws and milling machines have replaced human muscle during the rough shaping stage, but detailed shaping and finishing are still done by hand and by eye.

Such a pattern of 'small business' gunmaking also flourishes in Eibar in Spain, Ferlach in Austria, and around Gardone in Italy. So far as post-war sporting gun manufacture is concerned, there is little to choose between the quality of the very best English, Belgian, French and Italian houses, although, according to some observers, the average quality of Armi Famars in Italy or Georges Granger in France is now higher than that achieved in England.

Although the close connection with clockmaking ceased with the passing of the wheellock, it was not unusual for English gunmakers to pursue a subsidiary trade to sustain them in hard times: navigational and scientific instruments were favourites. Besides the high-quality gunmaker, serving a national or international clientele, and often specializing in a particular type or style of weapon, there existed everywhere numerous local gunsmiths. Some of these compared with the best. Others were and are competent 'practical gunsmiths', capable of

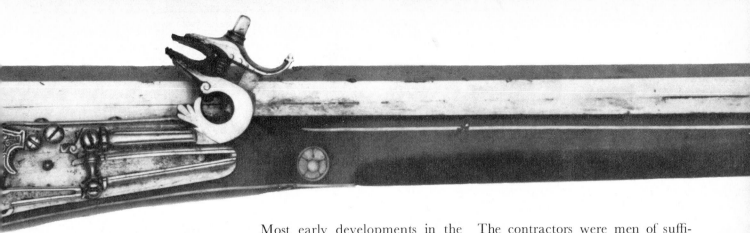

Flintlock carbine from the reign of James II (1685–88) made by Brooke whose name appears on the lockplate. The barrel is 31 in (78.7 cm) and the bullet was .69 in (17.5 mm) in diameter.

carrying out repairs and alterations, occasionally making a complete gun, but more often retailing an arm originating in Birmingham, Liège, Suhl, or wherever lay their national centre of mass production. Even if they 'made' guns, these gunsmiths often found it more economical and quicker to buy their locks or actions ready-made, a practice very common among the 'Pennsylvania' riflemakers of the Appalachian region of the United States in the late eighteenth to late nineteenth centuries. In America, this was only partly a question of technical ability, for in this period the costs of materials and transport, particularly of good steel, assumed far higher proportions of the final cost of an artefact than they do today.

Most early developments in the manufacturing process resulted from the needs of the military. In England during the sixteenth century there were a number of barrelmakers, lockmakers, stockers and inlayers working around the Minories, near the Tower of London, many of them of Dutch or German extraction. Some were members of the Armourers' Company, others of the Blacksmiths'. In 1581 Queen Elizabeth I was petitioned to set up a separate Livery Company, although this did not finally happen until 1638. During this period the gunmakers received unwelcome competition from cheap Dutch muskets, but were encouraged by a growing determination in the Council of War to introduce uniformity to the small arms of the army. The English Civil War (1642–8) brought administrative chaos, but the London gunmakers emerged relatively unscathed. The inevitable post-war slump, combined with an official policy of discouraging civilian ownership of arms, caused some men to leave the trade.

The Restoration in 1660 resulted in a sharp improvement in their economic lot, since there was not only a heavy demand for ceremonial arms but also a general military re-arming with improved matchlocks and new snaphaunce locks. From 1689, the gunmakers of Birmingham were also awarded military contracts, while muskets were still being purchased from Holland, such were the demands on the English to supply Ireland – where mass-production was deemed too risky – her American and West Indian colonies, and even her ally Portugal.

Arms at this period were obtained in lots of a few hundred to a few thousand from contractors, who would subcontract to pieceworkers the tasks of making locks and barrels.

The contractors were men of sufficient financial standing to be able to wait for payment, but they expected to receive a large eventual profit in compensation for such delays. The forces of the Crown were thus armed with a hodge-podge of firearms, acquired in various lots and with very approximately standardized bore sizes. The system was clearly inefficient, and improvements were needed. It had become clear that Birmingham did best at metalwork, particularly barrelmaking, while London's speciality was stockwork. Between 1715 and the 1750s, what is referred to today as the Ordnance system was set up, by which contracts for parts were let out to the specialist manufacturers, and most assembly was done by a specialized staff of the Small Gun Office in the Tower of London. By the mid-1750s, there is evidence not only that standardized gauges were being supplied to locksmiths in Birmingham, but that crucial measurements, such as bore size, were being specified in one-hundredths of an inch. Nevertheless, while the musket had been reasonably standardized in both England and France, the parts were not interchangeable. Muskets were still made by eye, copying pattern examples rather than following exact specifications and actual engineer's drawings.

The gun manufacturing centres in America, Britain and France were pretty much the same in the mid-eighteenth century, with major parts being part-made by water-powered machinery, which included trip hammers to forge skelp iron to form rough gun barrels and grinding mills to grind barrels, iron ramrods and bayonets into shape. Most finishing was done by hand, although water-powered barrel polishers had been developed.

The first serious attempt at a fully standardized weapon was the French musket of 1777, made using the *platines identiques* method. A precision-made pattern gauge of very hard steel was provided, and a semi-skilled workman used this as an exact guide while filing a gun-lock plate or lock part into shape from unhardened iron or steel. This did away with the need for skilled actioners, and made for speed, but was extremely hard on very expensive pattern gauges and files. The 1777 musket was, nevertheless, the first firearm whose manufacture was properly controlled, and as late as 1886 it was the proud boast of Les Fabricants d'Armes Réunis, a middle-sized Belgian company, that they made arms of 1777 quality. The system fascinated Benjamin Franklin, the American politician and statesman, who witnessed it in 1785 and recommended its immediate adoption in America. Nor did it pass unnoticed in England, where the Duke of Richmond, Master General of the Ordnance, pressed for a new form of mass-produced small-bore musket.

During the late eighteenth century, new materials became available to the gunsmith. In the 1770s, 'crucible' or 'cast' steel began to become available, and its relative purity made the production of reliable springs a more certain business. A process for making high-grade wrought iron, known as puddling, was introduced in England by Henry Cort in 1784, although it received little use in Belgium until 1834, or in the United States until 1870. Good steel was then at a premium, but plentiful, cheap steel suitable for gunmaking became available to all after 1855, with the introduction in England of the Bessemer process, in which carbon and other impurities were burned out by a blast of air forced through molten pig iron. This system was in general use by the mid-1860s.

From the opening years of the nineteenth century, however, there existed a strong and beautiful alternative to simple iron, at least for the manufacture of barrels for high-grade sporting weapons and gentlemen's pistols. The problem with ordinary iron was the high proportion of slag and other impurities that caused weak spots and a liability to burst. By the late eighteenth century, the best English makers were producing barrels made from the stubs of used horseshoe nails, which were believed to have been toughened by the constant pounding of the horse's hooves. They were hammered together at white heat to become a solid cake of iron, then drawn out into a long bar called a skelp, which was wound ribbon-fashion round a mandrel, the seam being 'jumped' (welded) together by hammering at high temperature. In fact their strength was gained by the hammering, which broke up and distributed impurities and slag, thus minimizing the chance of extensive flaws, and by the spiral seam, which was for practical purposes seamless in the plane of greatest stress, unlike a longitudinal join. When this surface was 'browned', a controlled rusting process that produced a beautiful soft, warm brown sheen, the stubs showed up in a pleasing light and dark pattern.

In Asia, these lamination processes had been much more highly developed, and barrels from India, Turkey and Kurdistan were known in Europe as being of the 'Damascus' type. They had a high reputation for strength which, it was believed, resulted from the tight twisting together of layers of ductile iron and strong steel. These twisted lengths

JUNE 28, 1862.   ILLUSTRATED TIMES.   145

THE WORKSHOPS OF ENGLAND. - No. VIII. MR. CHARLES REEVES'S IMPLEMENTS OF WAR MANUFACTORY, TOLEDO WORKS, BIRMINGHAM.

SWORD-BLADE, BAYONET, SWORD-BAYONET, AND MATCHETT GRINDING MILL.

GUN-BARREL ROLLING.

MOUNTING AND FINISHING SWORDS AND RIFLES.

BARREL-BORING, STRAIGHTENING, TURNING, AND POLISHING SHOP.

Samuel Colt was, in many ways, the first of the modern gunmakers, but others soon followed his lead in introducing machinery and line-production techniques. Charles Reeves worked in Birmingham from 1854—85, and this engraving of his premises dates from 1862.

Right
Birmingham was a great arms
centre during the nineteenth century,
but the majority of the gunmakers
operated in small groups. In this
part of a factory the barrels are
being ground to remove irregularities.

Below right
The proof house at Birmingham was
kept busy testing a steadily
increasing output from its
gunmakers in the nineteenth
century. Here the barrels, loaded
with a larger-than-normal charge,
are placed in the proof house ready
for firing. The engraving is from the
Illustrated London News of
February 1851.

were then hammered together to
form the skelp. The twisting produced beautiful complex patterns in
the metal, and these could be high-
lighted by acid etching which ate
away the soft iron more quickly than
the hard steel, and by browning.

The French and British Armies of
the Napoleonic Wars created such a
demand for arms that attempts at
standardization collapsed, particularly in Britain. There the simple
India Pattern musket became the
general-issue weapon, but a hetero-
geneous collection of arms was purchased, including French-pattern
muskets made by the Birmingham
company of Galton and Whately.
Although the patterns of arms multi-
plied, there was a definite tendency
towards mechanization among the
contractors.

The real incentive towards mechanization came from the United
States, where a perennial dearth of
competent mechanics spurred the
development of mass-production
techniques, a process begun by Eli
Whitney in 1809, in which machine
precision made up for lack of skill on
the operator's part. By 1817 Eli
Whitney's designs for power-driven
drill presses and fixed-spindle milling
machines were in wide use, and a
drop forge designed by Asa Waters
had almost trebled each workman's
barrel-making output in comparison
with the old skelp-and-mandrel
hand-welding process. Between 1818
and 1827 Thomas Blanchard designed a series of profile-cutting
machines for barrels, stocks and
eventually lock parts. These lathes
could turn irregular shapes, and
were 10 to 20 times faster than handwork. Precision gauging had begun
with the Hall breech-loader, and
Thomas Warner, the Master Armourer at the Government Arsenal
at Springfield, introduced precise
receiver gauges in the 1840s. By the
1850s, measurements were commonly specified in thousandths of an
inch. Power-driven rifling machines
were developed for Eli Whitney in
the 1840s, and in 1842 the system of
rough-forging components with a
single blow of a powerful drop
hammer was perfected by Albert
Eames of Chicopee, Massachusetts.
Such equipment required a high
degree of capital investment, and
thus naturally encouraged the
growth of large companies such as E
Remington & Sons, Eli Whitney,
and Robbins and Lawrence. The
Government Arsenals at Harper's
Ferry and Springfield were also
highly mechanized by the 1840s.

European eyes were opened to the
advantages of mass production by the
enormous cartwheel displays of ab-
solutely identical Colt revolvers at
the Great Exhibition in 1851, although a relatively high degree of
mechanization had already been
achieved in the government arms
works at Liège in Belgium. Steam-
driven machines had been introduced in the 1840s, each one manned
by a semi-skilled soldier trained to
carry out only one repetitive task. In
1854 a British purchasing mission
was sent to the United States to buy
equipment for the Enfield factory,
which went into full-scale mass production on the American system in
1856 under the eye of James Burton,
who was poached from Harper's

Ferry. The more enterprising and solvent contractors fought back by combining to create mechanized companies such as the London Small-arms Company, the National Arms and Ammunition Co. and the Birmingham Small Arms Company. These big companies existed mainly on military contracts, and a sudden restoration of peace could spell financial insecurity or even collapse. They produced a quality product with interchangeable parts, but their production lines were relatively inflexible, and large orders were a necessity. By contrast, the smaller hand-workers had low overheads, were sufficiently flexible to turn their hands to anything to meet the requirements of the customer, and could therefore undercut the big manufacturer. Thus in the early 1870s, a good machine-made American Remington rolling-block rifle cost £2 10s in England, the same price as a top-grade Birmingham machine-made interchangeable Snider. A hand-made Snider would retail for between £1 10s and £2 5s, depending on the finish.

Various attempts were made to limit the financial risk of the big companies. Remington developed a clever system of 'inside contracts', by which workers, machines and floor space were made available to a particular individual who had to pay his workers and make over a slice of the profits to Remington. If he succeeded in his endeavours, Remington gained. If he failed, Remington lost little or nothing. The real answer, however, was to diversify. BSA and FN in Belgium began to make bicycles and motor cars. Remington chose type-writers and chemicals. Winchester at one time made nearly everything from paint to refrigerators to garden tools to sports equipment to car tyres, and even ran their own chain of Woolworths-type stores, an endeavour killed off by the slump which crippled all growth in the 1930s.

Since World War II, government factories or contractors have concentrated on developing economical, expendable, purely military arms. Although several countries, the United States in particular, went through a 'cheap and cheerful' phase of civilian arms manufacture during the 1950s, with popular economy lines making wide use of stampings and plastics, there was soon a return to the old values of solid steel and good wood. Now the trick is to make a weapon that looks and feels as well-made as grandfather's hand-finished guns, but is reasonably economical to produce. This has been largely achieved through an increase in precision and through the development of moulding techniques so precise that engraving patterns can actually be cast in, and almost no hand-fitting and finishing is required.

While today's mass-produced rifle or shotgun may lack individuality, it is better-made than its forebears, and consists of better materials. In the fairly unlikely event of it breaking down, the offending part may expeditiously be replaced with the minimum of fuss. Matters were not always thus, and perhaps the earliest form of consumer protection was the proofing of arms. Since the late Middle Ages it was commonplace to prove sword blades for strength and for their cutting ability and to test plate armour by firing a powerful crossbow at it. In major centres of production, including Augsburg and Nuremberg, the guilds formed boards of inspection to check such arms and armour, and those that passed their inspection were marked with a control stamp. Such evidence of testing not only inspired confidence in the customer but served as a safeguard for the good name and reputation of the guild and its products.

The uncertain quality of early gun barrels made them an obvious candi-

Although modern technology has been able to simplify many of the processes, the 'best' sporting guns are still the result of much individual craftsmanship. Here the barrels are checked for any flaws by workers at Cogswell and Harrison, the London gunmakers.

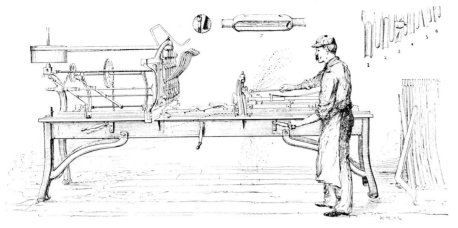

date for such testing, and by 1375 there is mention of cannon-barrel testing outside the Spalen Gate at Basle in Switzerland. Barrelmakers often stamped their own mark on small-arms barrels during the fifteenth-century, but after 1500 Nuremberg was applying city guild marks to gun barrels. Private proof by the better makers nevertheless remained the common pattern throughout the sixteenth and seventeenth centuries. The first serious attempt at setting up an independent testing body was incorporated in the Royal Charter of 1637 establishing the Worshipful Company of Gunmakers in London. This Charter makes alarming references to 'divers Blacksmiths and others inexpert in the Arte of Gunmaking' who 'have taken upon them to make try and prove Gunnes after their unskilfull way'. The result was that 'much harme and dannger through such unskilfulness in that Misterie hath happened to sondry of our loyall subjects'. In order to prevent these abuses, the Company was empowered to search, prove and mark all firearms made or imported for sale within a 10-mile radius of the City of London. Such 'foreign' arms of course included Birmingham guns. These powers were most certainly invoked, although an official Proof House was not established until 1713. The Worshipful Company of Gunmakers continues to administer the London Proofhouse, and is the only City livery company in which the exercise of its original controlling powers is still a primary function.

The activities of the Liège gunmakers were a constant source of anxiety to their ruling Prince-Bishop,

Above
The great government arsenal where Sergeant Major Jackson's rifle was made some 40 years earlier. Here a machine cuts a groove to hold the barrel of the Krag-Jorgensen rifles being made at Springfield Armoury in May 1899.

Right
Sergeant-Major William Jackson, 12th New York Volunteers Regiment, with his Springfield rifle Model 1855, drawn in 1869.

who attempted to institute compulsory proof in 1672. While the local makers were pleased to use the law as a protectionist measure to curb the sale of 'foreign' arms in their city, they were very reluctant to suffer the additional expense and delay themselves, particularly if they were volume producers of very cheap guns working on slim profit margins. It is safe to say that continuing attempts to impose proof laws in Liège, and in sundry other European cities, were unsuccessful until the nineteenth century.

In 1813, despite opposition from the London Proofhouse and their own less scrupulous brethren working at the cheap end of the trade, the better gunmakers of Birmingham obtained an Act of Parliament setting up their own proofhouse. The Act of 1813 for the first time made it an offence to sell any gun barrel in England or Wales that had not first been proved in London or Birmingham. As modified in 1815, this legislation was rigorously enforced. Similar legislation was passed in Belgium in 1836, and gradually other European nations followed suit.

Belgium and England later established a fairly standard method of proofing guns. An arm was first 'viewed' to check for any obvious flaws in material or workmanship. If it passed this visual inspection, it was then subjected to one or more firings, using a substantial overload. Providing no damage had been caused, the Proofhouse would then stamp on one or more marks. There is no independent proof of firearms in America, the cradle of consumer protection. It is probably fair to say that today there is no need for such legislation, since the Courts there are prepared to award such astronomical damages to injured consumers that no manufacturer can afford to market unsafe arms.

A practice of unilateral recognition of other countries' proof marks began to occur, the lead being taken by Germany, and a Conference on Proof was held in Brussels in 1914. As a result, the governments of Austria, Belgium, France, Germany, Great Britain, Italy and Spain agreed to accept each other's proof marks – a remarkable and even paradoxical example of pan-European co-operation on the very brink of World War I.

179

Exotica

Frederick Wilkinson

It is ironic that the part of the world which was responsible for the discovery of gunpowder had to wait for centuries before firearms began to play any real part in its history. It was the Portuguese seamen who took the firearm back to the Orient. During the fifteenth century their ships probed south in the Atlantic until, eventually, they rounded the Cape of Good Hope and reached India in 1498. As their skill and daring increased the Portuguese navigators pushed farther to the east; by 1514 they had made contact with Pekin in China, and in 1543 they made a landfall in Japan. The local warriors and nobility of all these places viewed them with a mixture of scorn and fear but they could not fail to be impressed by their powerful weapons. Soon they demanded matchlock muskets like the Portuguese carried.

The native craftsmen were quite capable of producing copies of the matchlock but they modified the design and made changes in detail. In India the stock was made longer, thinner and generally straighter, with little or no widening to the butt. In section it was rectangular or polygonal and was sometimes decorated with brass, mother of pearl, coral or similar materials. Barrels were usually fairly long with a comparatively small bore and were secured to the stock by bands of metal, known as capucines, or bound on with leather. Like the stock the barrel was often decorated with applied brass.

The ignition system of the Indian matchlock, the torador, was not mounted on a plate and then affixed to the stock, but was usually set directly into the wood, leaving only the end part of the serpentine visible. For some reason which is not clear, the Indian gunsmiths reversed the

Above
This carbine was probably made in Turkey. The barrel has applied gold decoration and the butt is of the typical pentagonal shape. The lock is similar to the European miquelet with a finger bar fitted at the top of the cock to ensure a good grip when cocking the action. Wallace Collection, London

Right
Repeating matchlock carbine from India. The six charges are contained in the cylinder and this was rotated by hand to bring each, in turn, into line with the barrel. The serpentine holding the match is raised clear of the pan. The redwood stock has some simple inlay. Wallace Collection, London.

direction of the movement of the serpentine. On the European matchlock it swung back in the direction of the butt to press the match into the pan, but on Indian weapons it moved in the opposite direction, swinging towards the muzzle. The priming pan was usually smaller than European types but it did have a simple cover and many of the weapons had a small metal spike attached to the lock by a short length of chain. This

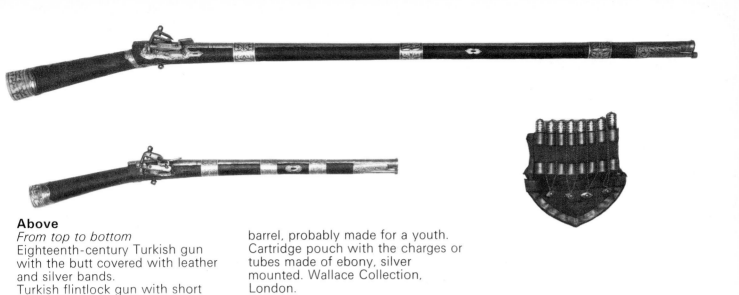

Above

From top to bottom
Eighteenth-century Turkish gun with the butt covered with leather and silver bands.
Turkish flintlock gun with short barrel, probably made for a youth. Cartridge pouch with the charges or tubes made of ebony, silver mounted. Wallace Collection, London.

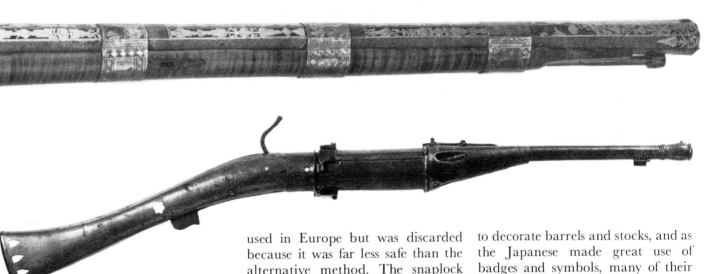

was a pricker to clear the touch-hole of any fouling.

Japanese gunsmiths designed their weapons with thick-walled, heavy barrels, often with a thick moulding at the muzzle. Most had a simple set of sights. The majority of Japanese matchlocks had fairly short barrels and the stocks had a stubby or chunky appearance with only a short butt. As in the Indian weapons the serpentine moves forwards, but the Japanese adopted a different mechanical system. On European and Indian weapons the serpentine was held clear of the pan by the pressure of a spring and the action of the trigger forced it down against this spring. The Japanese system worked in the opposite manner with the spring forcing the serpentine down. This system, the snaplock, had been used in Europe but was discarded because it was far less safe than the alternative method. The snaplock was prepared by raising the serpentine, so compressing the spring, and it was then locked up by a sear. Pressure on the trigger withdrew the sear so allowing the serpentine to fall and press the glowing match into the pan. Obviously any pressure or knock on the trigger could so easily cause an accident but, despite its apparent disadvantages, the system was retained by the Japanese until the nineteenth century.

Another peculiarity of Japanese weapons was the use of brass instead of steel for the springs. Japanese metal workers were the equal of any in the world but apparently they just did not like making steel springs. The brass spring is much less positive and the Japanese action has a characteristically soft, soggy feel to it. The Japanese also seem to have disliked making screws, for they secured the barrels and locks to the stock with pins. Brass, gold and silver were used to decorate barrels and stocks, and as the Japanese made great use of badges and symbols, many of their matchlocks bear the 'mon' or family badge of the owner.

Apart from a tenuous trade link, mainly with the Dutch, the Japanese cut themselves off from all contact with the West and consequently later forms of ignition for firearms were not adopted for their weapons. It was not until 1854, when an American expedition led by Commodore Perry visited Japan that contact was re-established. After this, the Japanese adopted and adapted Western technology. The firearms manufacturers went, almost in one step, from matchlock to cartridge weapons. Very few examples of Japanese flintlock or percussion weapons exist.

The newer systems did, however, influence other Asiatic firearms and the flintlock, in various forms, was used. In the Balkans and bordering countries the miquelet form of the flintlock was common. The Iranian (Persian) and Turkish version tends to be rather squat with a small, rectangular frizzen and the cock also has squarish jaws. Although the sparking action is the same as on other flintlocks the miquelet's mechanical system is different. Instead of an internal tumbler the sear operates through the lockplate, engaging directly with the cock to lock it in place. Pressure on the trigger withdraws the sear, allowing the cock to swing forward. Many of the firearms from this area are very ornate with all forms of applied decoration, precious metals, enamels, semi-precious stones, embroidery and fringes.

India was very much under the influence of France and England, and the style of flintlock which was adopted there was normally of conventional form. Many of the weapons from the sub-continent are fitted with European-made locks sold by the East India Company, which held a trading monopoly. Such locks normally carry the company's mark, which is a quartered heart or a lion, and they are often dated.

The native craftsman fashioning a gun knew that certain markings seemed to enhance the value of the weapon. It was not uncommon for them to copy these marks from European weapons on to their own pieces. Sometimes the marks were partly obliterated or the craftsmen could not quite master them, and some weapons bear strange variants of 'LONDON MADE' or 'WARRANTED', and the names of famous London makers appear on pieces that would never have graced their workshops.

East of India, the flintlock seems to have been rarely used by native craftsmen, and most areas retained the matchlock up to this century. There seems to have been little attempt by Asiatic gunsmiths to develop or improve on their traditional firearm. However, some repeating matchlocks were made in India with a cluster of chambers which were rotated manually to bring each in turn under the match; similar Japanese weapons are also known. One European weapon which was taken up and developed by Turkish and Indian smiths was

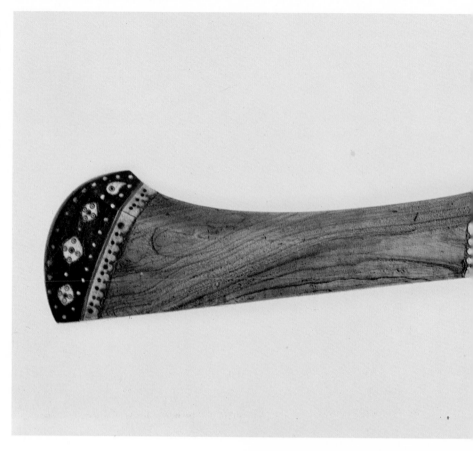

Above
Butt and lock of a typical Indian torador. Only the tip of the serpentine protrudes from the stock, which is inlaid with pieces of decorated horn. The barrel is secured by leather binding.

Right
Butt and lock from an Afghan or Scinde flintlock. The lockplate is dated 1814 and bears the East India Company's symbol of a lion. The stock is decorated with applied brass and simple inlay.

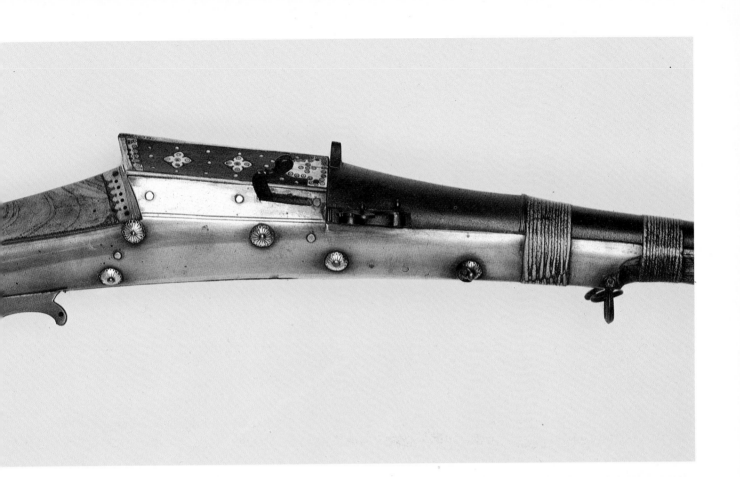

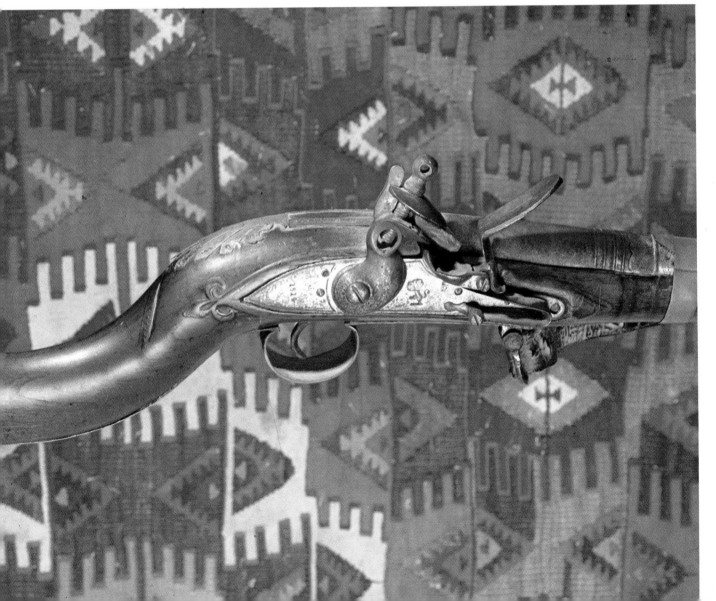

Above
Huzzarehs from the Punjab fire their matchlocks with attached bipods. British troops fighting in the campaign of 1849 found their enemies skilled snipers with such weapons.

Right
Swivel-mounted blunderbuss, *circa* 1780. The lock is marked 'Tower' and the weapon could well have been mounted on a ship. The butt is stamped with a Birmingham gunmaker's mark. G. Kellam, Broadstairs, Kent.

Above
Brass-barrelled blunderbuss by
Mortimer of London. It has a spring-
operated, folding bayonet fitted
above the barrel.

Left
Skinner's Horse, a native regiment
of light cavalry, attack at the Battle
of Bhurtpore in 1826. They carry
their matchlocks across their backs
while using the lance and sword.

Below
Butt and lock of a Kurdish
flintlock. The butt is polygonal in
section and has characteristic bands
and geometric inlaid decoration.
The small ball trigger is also typical
of such weapons.

the blunderbuss. The idea behind the
Donderbuss, or blunderbuss, was that
a number of missiles discharged
simultaneously stood a better chance
of hitting a target than a single shot.
In the sixteenth century some short-
barrelled weapons were loaded with
a number of bullets to get this
advantage, but it was not until the
seventeenth century that the blunderbuss began to develop. It was
obvious that the load of bullets
spread out as they left the barrel. It
was therefore reasoned that if the
muzzle was opened out then the
spread would be greater. This is true
up to a point, but beyond this point a
wider muzzle has little or no effect on
the spread. The Indian gunmaker
was unaware of this fact and went on
to spread the barrel wider and wider;
the results were often grotesque with
barrels approaching caricature proportions. The Turkish gunsmiths

took the blunderbuss and proceeded
to reduce it from a two-handed
shoulder weapon to a pistol-type
arm. In shape and design it is the
same as the full-sized weapon but it is
small enough to be used in one hand.

In Europe, and Britain in particular, the blunderbuss was popular as a
'self-defence' weapon and was carried
on coaches as well as being kept
handy by the door or bed. The
barrels were of brass or iron and
some had an obvious flare to the
barrel, whilst others had cylindrical
barrels with a bore which gradually
widened as it neared the muzzle.
Large versions of the blunderbuss
were sometimes mounted on swivels
and used as wall-pieces for defending
fortified points. Another use was in
clearing a ship's deck of boarders.

In an attempt to make the blunderbuss even more effective as a

Blunderbuss of the early nineteenth century with the bayonet 'sprung' and ready for action. Marked Ketland. W. Keith Neal, Guernsey.

weapon, many were fitted with a spring-operated blade on the barrel. The idea was apparently first tried early in the eighteenth century but it does not seem to have become popular for several decades. A system was patented in 1781 by John Waters, a Birmingham gunmaker, although he only claimed the patent for pistols. The blade, usually triangular in section, was commonly fitted on the top of the barrel and pivoted at the muzzle. When not required the blade was folded back along the barrel so compressing a small, but strong V-spring. The tip of the blade was held by some form of catch and when this was released the blade swung forward and locked in place.

When the percussion system was introduced many blunderbusses were modified to take the new action, but the percussion pepperbox pistol and revolver began to displace the blunderbuss as a self-defence weapon. The newer firearms were so much smaller and less difficult to carry than the blunderbuss. One of the most unusual blunderbusses was one which combined the flared barrel with the idea of a revolver. Beckwith, a London gunmaker, made one model blunderbuss which had six rotating flared barrels!

Although gunpowder and, later, smokeless powder were the prime means of generating the power to discharge a missile, they were by no means the only ones. The power of moving air had long been used to speed missiles on their way, and blowpipes, whilst not common, were not unknown in Europe. It is therefore hardly surprising that experiments were used at an early date to use the force of moving air to discharge a bullet.

One of the earliest references is contained in the notes of Leonardo da Vinci, and Marin le Bourgeoys, the French gunsmith largely responsible for the standard flintlock, experimented and produced a very efficient example of an air gun which was said to fire its projectile up to 400 paces. There was even talk in 1655 of a plan to use an air gun to assassinate Oliver Cromwell, Republican ruler of England. During the seventeenth century there were many experiments using air as a propulsive force. Given plenty of equipment and material it is not difficult to generate sufficient power to force out the projectile. The problem lies in the means of so doing when there are severe restrictions on the acceptable space and weight available.

Generally speaking, all air guns work on one of three systems: a short burst of moving air generated by a plunger driven forward by a spring, the sudden compression of a bellows, or a supply of air under pressure from some sort of reservoir. The earliest weapons usually favoured the simplest method, which used the spring-operated plunger. By one means or other – a small handle to wind it up with, or a lever of some sort – a spring was compressed. When the trigger was pressed the spring was released and its forward movement quickly pushed the plunger along a chamber to build up sufficient pressure to blow the missile out of the barrel. Weapons of this type enjoyed a certain degree of popularity during the sixteenth century but then they rather fell out of use until the mid-nineteenth century, when they enjoyed a brief vogue particularly in the United States where they were used mainly for target shooting on indoor ranges. From 1876 cheap, spring-operated air guns came on to the market. They were introduced by Henry Marcus Quackenbush of New York, who devised a weapon made up of pressed metal and a very simple mechanism. The Quackenbush system is still used in many cheap modern weapons. On Quackenbush's first model the spring was compressed by the simple expedient of placing the muzzle on some solid surface and pressing the barrel back into the body of the weapon.

Bellows guns operated in a similar fashion, although in them the spring compressed a small bellows rather than pushing forward a piston. This form of air gun seems to have originated in Central Europe, in the Austrian-Czechoslovakian region. They were frequently made to look exactly like a wheellock or flintlock gun, complete with locks, although the bellows was situated in the butt.

Bellows-operated guns were made right through the eighteenth and nineteenth centuries, and it has been suggested that they were mostly used for firing darts rather than ball ammunition. Most of the later examples are breech-loading, and this would be a very important feature if darts were the main projectile.

The power generated by these bellows and spring plungers was limited, and the weapons which gave maximum power and enjoyed most popularity were the type fitted with a reservoir to hold compressed air. The reservoir had to be strong enough to withstand quite considerable pressure, and it represented an added complication since it had to be housed somewhere on the weapon. The early weapons fitted it concentrically around the barrel whilst others had the reservoir housed within the butt. Late in the seventeenth century a third form was developed: this was globular and was usually screwed on to the stock beneath the

Above
Firing systems for air rifles.
From top to bottom.
German air rifle with brass reservoir.
Spring plunger air rifle from Germany with cocking lever.
London-made air gun with reservoir above the breech. The silver fittings are hallmarked for 1777.

Below
From top to bottom.
Austrian military air rifle with butt reservoir and magazine along the side of the barrel.
Similar model but a civilian version, made in Vienna.
Another version by Ridiger, with a leather-covered butt.
All these weapons were made *circa* 1780–90.

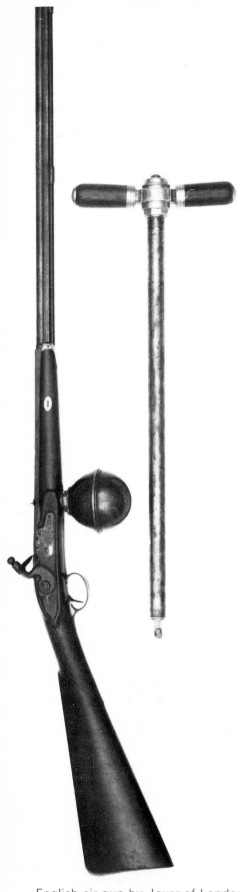

English air gun by Jover of London, made about 1780. It has multi-groove rifling and a large copper reservoir which was unscrewed so that it could be filled under pressure with the hand pump, also shown.

breech. Whichever form the reservoir took it had to be filled with compressed air. This was done by means of a pump – a time-consuming and physically exhausting business.

The reservoirs held sufficient air to power a number of shots. They were variously shaped but the most popular with sportsmen was the globe. Despite its large volume it had one advantage in that the gun could be made in the conventional form and the reservoir attached at some convenient point, usually below the breech. They do seem to have been rather liable to burst, however, and a number of fatal accidents was recorded, which had a limiting effect on their popularity!

The air weapon which saw most use was that adopted by the Austrian Army. A watchmaker, Bartholomew Girandoni of the Tyrol, designed a breech-loading weapon with a detachable reservoir which also served as the butt. The new weapon, Pattern 1780, was a 13-mm rifle with a magazine of 20 balls fitted beside the barrel. A pump was supplied and around 1,500 strokes were required to create the right pressure, said to be sufficient to discharge the last of 20 balls with an effective range of 120 paces.

The Girandoni weapon was issued during the war between Austria and Turkey in 1788, each rifle equipped with two spare magazines. In 1790 a special Sharpshooters group was formed. The weapons saw spasmodic service right through to the Napoleonic campaigns of 1815 and were even resurrected during a rebellion in 1848–49. It was claimed by one French general that men found using the weapon were not considered true soldiers and were hanged on capture, although the particular incident to which he referred seems to have been an isolated one.

The idea of steam being used as a means of propulsion was explored, and there are a number of references to such weapons, some of which seem to have been reasonably efficient. There were obviously great practical problems in generating the steam and these guns never became generally popular. At least one workable model was produced by Jacob Perkins of Newport, USA. In 1824 he constructed a device which was said to have fired 240 rounds in one minute. Despite its proven ability the weapon was just not practical since the ancillary equipment was far too heavy and bulky – its water consumption was enormous – to be of use in the field.

Gas generated by other means was also considered and although little is known for certain it seems reasonably sure that the first efforts in the early part of the nineteenth century aimed at using the properties of solid carbon dioxide which was first produced around this period.

One of the most intriguing methods of propulsion was one demonstrated by Thomas Beningfeld in 1845, which was electrically detonated. It was demonstrated to a group of British officers who were quite impressed by its performance. However, a certain impasse arose because Beningfeld refused to disclose to the committee, including the Duke of Wellington, the method of detonation. The committee just as firmly refused to consider the weapon at all until they knew how it worked, and to this day it is not clear how the explosive power was generated. The electric gun was said to fire up to 1,200 shots a minute and certainly, when demonstrated, it made a favourable impression. A gunmaker later suggested that the detonation was achieved by decomposing water into hydrogen and oxygen by electricity supplied by a large battery.

Man's ingenuity in finding methods of discharging a missile has been considerable. If all the time, effort, money and thought devoted to weapons had been channelled into more constructive areas, who knows what could have been achieved!

Index

Figures in *italic* refer to illustrations.

190